THE
FLYING MACHINE
Its Evolution through the Ages

To The Lady
who grips me tight at take-off

Allen Andrews

THE
FLYING MACHINE
Its Evolution through the Ages

G. P. Putnam's Sons New York

CONTENTS

Library of Congress Catalog Card Number:
77-75933
SBN: 399-11967-1

First American Edition 1977
© Allen Andrews 1977

This book was first published in Great Britain,
under the title: *BACK TO THE DRAWING
BOARD*

Printed in Great Britain

LIST OF ILLUSTRATIONS

1 IMPOSSIBLE DREAM

'I dream things that never were', said the Serpent to Eve at the foot of the Tree of Knowledge. 'And I say: "Why not?"' Aeronautics is the outstanding example in human history of the race wanting to do something supernatural for the whole of its cerebral tool-wielding existence, and finally achieving the impossible dream.

Men and women flew in the twentieth century because they had been dreaming of flying for 2,000 centuries previously. The sensation was ecstatic. We sought to re-create that exaltation in waking life. We were practical poets, and we were bloodily broken. The dream persisted.

Finally success came to some of us. We few, we happy few, we band of brothers became aeronauts. The rest of us became passengers. The first passengers still caught the ecstasy. We could hear the hiss of substantial air being cleft by the tremulous aerofoil; we could fear death with the feel of the fog in our throat, the mist in our face. Then air travel became bland, like the pap of airborne food; we were inducted into pressurised caskets and had to exercise the mind very

Members of the Aeronautical Society of Great Britain with Hiram Maxim's 'Flying Machine', 1894. At this time Otto Lilienthal, the greatest man in aeronautics before the Wright brothers, was building a new carbonic acid gas engine to attempt powered flight. He died in 1896 from a broken spine after stalling in a monoplane glider while advancing his experiments to achieve responsible control of an aeroplane in flight—a necessity which only he and the Wrights then fully recognised.

hard to recapture the exhilaration of suspense between the illusion of immortality and the fear of death.

In following their dream aeronauts have used all the mechanical and intellectual genius available to them. Accomplishment has become corporate. But the fulfilment is still the individual driver's. The urge to fly is basically romantic. It is a personal achievement, like sailing or making love, with which it has some affinities. However passive the vegetable freight behind him may be, the driver is still an aeronaut: an *aeronaut* and not an *aviator*, as the linguistic impurists insist on calling him. He is sailing in air, navigating a craft by man-developed skill—not flapping avian wings of the crudest un-avian design, not using (because he has no power to use) instinctive reactions to magnetism, pressure, solar and stellar configurations and a biological chronometer, which are endowed in the equipment of the bird. Birdmen have been brave, doomed, dead-end blunderers in the progress of aeronautics.

2 ICARUS AND ALL ANGELS

Inevitably bird flight became incorporated into the early dream as the readiest image of the new dimension. There are physical and psychological explanations of the dreams of flying, which are now seriously accepted as the emotional stimulus that incubated our desire to fly until flight was within our technical competence. Dreams of soaring flight are said to be a manifestation of what Jung called the collective unconscious, the residue of all our ancestral experiences. Our archaic ancestry includes recognition of that period in our evolution when we swam effortlessly in the sea and below it: physically we retain from this stage the vestiges of gills (the Eustachian tubes between the middle ear and the throat, which now redress imbalances of pressure at different altitudes). When we dream of soaring, we are said to recapture the easy motion of that earlier existence, though psychologists are quick to add an extra, nearer memory of exaltation after orgasm. Soaring is sometimes merged in a dream with a sensation of controlled falling, the result being a series of rather strenuous kangaroo hops in the upper air. A dead stall—the dream sensation

On either side of a sacred tree connecting Hell, Earth and Heaven stand winged gods of Babylon in a carving 3,000 years old.

of sharply falling—has a direct biological link with the change in the rhythm of the heart that occurs in sleep and is most commonly noticed in the familiar shock, caused by a sudden fall in blood pressure, which happens when we are 'dropping off'. This irregularity in the heart can be artificially induced by a poisonous drug that was once self-administered by witches. When witches, under torture, confessed that they had flown, they may well have believed that they had; but they had been flying under the influence of aconite and in the confusion of belladonna intoxication, and in reality had never left the ground.

What made flight mystical—even the simulation of flight in dreams—was the fact that the gods flew. We have the records that confirm this fundamental belief, which is almost as old as religion. Five thousand years of pictorial art show the ancient gods as lords of the air. The representation of God often began as the depiction of a bird: Horus, the god from whom the Pharaohs descended, was a falcon. Winged gods and goddesses were portrayed in Babylonia, Assyria

and Anatolia long before they were sculpted in Greece; but it was in Greece that the physical beauty of coordinated flight was best understood. The Nike (Winged Victory) of Samothrake, carved about 195 BC, represents a patron goddess, after bestowing a naval victory, alighting in easy majesty to be a living figurehead on the prow of a ship. She still has forward momentum as she copes with the head wind while landing, and the interplay between the moving air, the body's draperies and the human figure has never been better expressed.

God's messengers were recognised as winged angels by many religions. The Greeks were generally somewhat miserly in allocating wings: even Hermes (the Roman Mercury), the herald of the gods, was issued only with a winged hat and winged sandals, though he was of full godly rank—self-appointed, it is true, after he had selected himself as twelfth man on Olympus. The Zoroastrians in ancient Iran *created* angels in the eighth century BC when Zarathrustra, striving to establish monotheism, demoted all gods but one to the rank of archangel. Among the Jews at exactly the same time (750 BC) the prophet Isaiah first described seraphim, who were stationed *above* the throne of the Lord, as follows: 'each one had six wings: with twain he covered his face, and with twain he covered his feet, and with twain he did fly.' (This early adoption into basic flying of a streamlined fuselage and a blind-flying simulator is unique.)

The Jews had four orders of angels in their hierarchy—archangels, angels, seraphim and cherubim. For the Christians St Paul added five more—thrones, dominions, principalities, powers and virtues. The Moslems accepted angels: it was Gabriel who brought from heaven to the prophet Mohammed the sacred revelation of the *Koran.*

God was Lord of the Air. Most of our ideas of God have developed from beliefs that began in the Near East. Here is Ashur, the supreme god of the Assyrians, as portrayed in a marble bas-relief of about 1000 BC.

Mohammed regarded angels as military auxiliaries: when, in the second year of the Hegira (AD 623), he was commander of a band of 305 men from Medina who defeated an expeditionary force from Mecca numbering 1,000, he declared that squadrons of angels had come down to reinforce him in his battle.

Because angels were divine, the theological establishment of all religions has taught that mortal men who tried to fly were guilty of impiety for aping god, and were guaranteed to come to a bad end. Since the theologians controlled the poets and myth-makers, all the folk-tales of rash men trying to fly culminated (with one exception) in the previously built-in disaster. The ancient Greeks had several moral tales constructed to this specification. Helios, the Sun God, daily drove his four-horse chariot across the sky from his magnificent palace in the east to the Islands of the Blessed in the west—neatly connecting with the departure of a golden ferryboat that carried him and his transport overnight to his eastern point of departure. One of the seven sons of Helios was Phaethon, who was always pestering him to be allowed to drive the chariot for one day. Helios finally consented. But the inexperienced Phaethon could not control his flaming team, first driving them so high that the earth froze, and then so low that it scorched. Zeus, king of the gods, outraged by this inexpert piloting, launched a thunderbolt that killed Phaethon, whose body fell into the Po, an ultimate fate far worse than death to the trembling tyro airmen who heard this cautionary tale in England, where the river had a peculiar significance.

Bellerophon, another adventurous youngster, wrought a number of daring deeds, including the slaying of the fiery Chimaera. He accomplished this by capturing the winged horse Pegasus, which he bridled and urged into the air; and from this gun platform he strafed the Chimaera with arrows from above, weaving tight circles as he worked his bow. Finally he dropped an ingenious incendiary, using his superior height to thrust a lump of lead between the monster's

The angel Gabriel reveals the *Koran* to the prophet Mohammed.

14

The impulsive Icarus crashes into the sea, while Daedalus flies grimly on.

The god Hermes, herald of Zeus, with wings confined to his hat and heels.

15

jaws. The Chimaera's fiery breath melted the lead, which trickled down its throat and cauterised its vitals. Understandably elated with his success, Bellerophon determined to fly Pegasus on a lap of honour that was to include a high-altitude docking at Olympus, the home of the gods. But Zeus interpreted this proposal as a presumptuous claim to immortality. He sent a gadfly, which stung the ascending Pegasus in a vulnerable spot under the tail. The horse reared, and Bellerophon was thrown down, landing in a thorn bush, from whose pricks he never fully recovered. Pegasus limped heavenward with a punctured tank, but was punitively transferred from Strike Command to an auxiliary transport role, and worked out his time toting thunderbolts around the sky while a reclining Zeus decided where to launch them.

Daedalus, a son of the royal house of Athens, was a natural inventor and trained himself, with some help from the goddess Athene, to be a superb craftsman-mechanic. Like other inventors, he was not without professional jealousy, and when his nephew forestalled him by inventing the saw, Daedalus took the lad up to the top of the Acropolis to admire the view and threw him off the roof of the Parthenon. For this slip of the hand he was exiled to Crete, where he was speedily granted a royal warrant as fixer to the court. He built for the monarch's wife Pasiphae, who had an unnatural ambition to couple with a bull, a frame of cowhide in which the lady concealed herself and achieved the desired consummation. King Minos of Crete, excusably put out at the part Daedalus had played in the begetting of the Minotaur on his wife, ordered a search-and-destroy operation against him all over the island. Daedalus escaped by making two pairs of wings, one for his son Icarus and one for himself. Though the quill feathers were strung together with thread, the tips of the wings (the primaries) were held in place by wax. Daedalus begged Icarus not to fly too near the sun, for fear of the wax melting; nor to swoop too low, when the feathers might become waterlogged with sea-spray. But Icarus was so exhilarated by the experience of flying that he beat upwards towards the sun. The wax duly melted, and Icarus crashed into the sea.

All airmen have a natural sympathy with Icarus, deriving a certain morbid pleasure from the drama that the gods are always against them. But they deprive themselves of eternal justification by ignoring the success of Daedalus, who methodically flew some 750 miles and touched down at Cumae, near Naples, where no doubt his wings were on offer in the local black market that very evening. Daedalus, in fact, the eternal cheeky chappie, was never fazed throughout his career. From Naples he secured an appointment to the court of Sicily, where Minos eventually tracked him down in the king's palace. But Daedalus, who was getting on extremely well with the king's daughters, persuaded them to suggest a warm bath for Minos with the promise of better things to come. The bath-house was of Daedalus' own construction, and while Minos was floating in perfumed ease, Daedalus poured molten pitch down a supernumerary pipe and blotted out his enemy.

3 BIRDMEN AND TOWER-JUMPERS

Chinese history, which is often surprisingly reliable in its dating—as checked with eclipses mentioned in the annals and now back-calculated by modern astronomers—mentions that in the year 2250 BC the Emperor Shun, then a boy, escaped from a hill prison by 'putting on the working clothes of a bird'. He never forgot this successful glide to safety and, when he was a man, jumped off a tower with his hands gripping lines attached to two large circular hats as his only means of support. History glosses over any injuries he sustained, but it was notable that he was succeeded by the Emperor Yü, 'who was called to the throne on account of his ability as an engineer'.

Emperors and kings seem to have been particularly fascinated by wing-flapping and tower-jumping. In the West the legendary tenth king of Britain, Bladud, the monarch who discovered the curative properties of the Bath waters and was the father of King Lear, is recorded as having made an attempt to show off his technical powers to the populace by flying over London in a bird suit with, as an auxiliary engine, the power of his 'necromantic arts'. After a few evolutions in the air, his wings failed him. He fell down on the temple of Apollo and broke his neck, which was more than the waters of Bath could cure. The alleged date of this fatal crash was 852 BC, but the British records cannot be so accurate as the Chinese, for the episode was not written up until exactly 2,000 years later, in Geoffrey of Monmouth's *History of the Kings of Britain* in 1148.

By this time there were better authenticated instances of tower-jumpers using artificial wings. The Arab Abbasa Ben Firnasa fluttered to death at Cordoba in AD 890. Elmer, a Benedictine monk of Malmesbury, Wiltshire, jumped from a tower and was airborne for 200yd before spinning and breaking his legs; the date was about 1130, but the earliest existing record of the folk-tale dates from 1648, when it was inserted in the *History of Britain* by John Milton, who later consolidated his interest in fallen angels by writing *Paradise Lost*.

In 1490 an Italian mathematician, Giovanni Battista Danti, was said to have soared on wings over Lake Trasimeno in Umbria. In

Pancake landing imminent: the Marquis de Bacqueville somewhat fancifully 'frozen' in mid-flight between the Quai Voltaire and the waters of the Seine, 1742.

The wing motion of a strong flying bird shows how it proceeds by tractor propulsion. The power stroke (left) begins downwards, but the primary feathers at the tips of the wings are angled upwards and forwards so that they screw into the air, and the main wing follows forwards. On the up-stroke (right) the primaries separate limply to decrease air resistance, but the general backward movement of the main wing keeps the forward motion in operation.

1503 he jumped from the top of his parish church in Perugia, and was reported as having sailed for 300 paces before a strut in his left wing collapsed. He hit another church tower and eventually died, lamenting the popularity of religion in the city. In 1507 another Italian, Giovanni Damian, who had been appointed physician to the Scottish court and Abbot of Tongland in Kirkcudbright, took off in a cloud of feathers from the battlements of Stirling Castle. He announced that he was making for France, but only reached the castle dung-heap, a soft landing that merely broke his thigh.

The activities of Danti and Damian coincided with the intense interest in birdman flying evinced by Leonardo da Vinci, who in the 1490s became obsessed with duplicating the wing-flapping of birds, and designed ornithopters to imitate this motion. But genius as he was in other spheres of aeronautics—he invented prototypes of the parachute, the retractable undercarriage, the airscrew, and re-invented the helicopter—he was doomed to failure in simulating bird-flight because, not having high-speed photography, he never understood it. He did not kill anybody, but his assistant mechanic, Astro Peretola, did surreptitiously try out one set of his wings, which, being 72ft across, snagged in a tree before worse befell.

It was physically impossible before the advent of a lightweight mechanical system to fit out a man with the propulsive apparatus of a bird (soaring flight is a little easier) for three reasons: man's unsuitable airframe, puny muscles, and ignorance of the dynamics of driving flight. A bird has hollow bones, often, as with an eagle, having internal struts to reinforce the strength while restricting the weight. But the delicate skeleton has a rigid spine and a broad strong shield of a breast-bone with a deep keel to it—visible even in the carcass of a domestic chicken. The 'airframe' is not only an extraordinarily well designed functional combination of lightness and strength, but it places the centre of gravity of the bird in a far more efficient flying

Léo Valentin in the gear he devised for free-fall gliding. 'I have flown like a bird for more than three miles', he said. 'That's not a bad beginning. I shall have to improve the wing profile, increase the lift and streamline the body. One day I shall probably be able to land'. But Valentin was flung to the earth as ruthlessly as other pioneers.

19

position than in, say, a man swimming the butterfly stroke, which is the nearest practical human movement to wing-flapping. The rigid keeled breast-bone, however, allows plenty of surface for the adhesion of the very powerful flight muscles—proportionately far stronger than in a man, and fuelled and cooled by many auxiliary lungs supplying the necessary oxygen—which a bird calls on when using its wings for driving forward flight. A man simply has insufficient muscle to propel his wrongly balanced, ill designed airframe forward by additionally heavy artificial wings without mechanical means. He could neither find the requisite energy nor survive the overheating of his body.

Furthermore, even Leonardo—and every ornithopter-designer until the nineteenth century—completely missed the trick a bird performs between two and eighty times a second (according to the species) when it drives its wings in forward flight. Leonardo said that the wings 'row downwards and backwards, like swimming in water'. In fact they go downwards and forwards, and the primary feathers of the wing-tips do not passively flap but actively screw into the forward air to draw the bird on with tractor propellers. No man, madly flapping outsize wings at a required speed faster than his metabolism can maintain, has the additional expertise to twist his feather-clad fingers like a demented harpist to work false primaries.

Nevertheless the pure birdmen gallantly continued their hopeless course. In 1742 the Marquis de Bacqueville thought he could fly across the Seine with four individual insect-wings on arms and legs. Originally he thought his valet could do it, but the servant declined on a point of precedence. The Marquis took off from the Quai Voltaire and crashed on a washerwoman's raft in midstream. A Russian copied the Emperor Shun exactly and escaped from a fortress on canvas wings. But he was recaptured and made to do it again. He merely fluttered down to the stake that had been erected to burn him in the courtyard as a sorcerer. In 1874 the Belgian De Groof cast off from a captive balloon 900ft above Cremorne Gardens, by the Thames, gliding on two broad wings and a 20ft tail, which he worked by hands and feet from a vertical frame. He survived the first drop with a bruised tail, but killed himself on the encore.

Finally came the last obstinate idealists, who jumped from powered aircraft. Clem Sohn, the American, died at Vincennes in 1937 when he jumped from 9,000ft, glided to 1,800ft on canvas wings, then pulled a double Roman candle on his main and reserve parachutes and plummeted to earth. The lovable Léo Valentin, who taught modern free-fall parachutists much of what they know, changed from canvas to wooden wings weighing, with the necessary corset, 30lb, and in 1954 over Thorigny at 9,000ft he glided three miles on his wings before parachuting to earth. But nature was only delaying her declaration of mastery over those who advance human muscles alone against the force of elemental air. Valentin was wrenched into impotence and cast to the ground with his wings crushed. He is dead, the last of a line of dedicated men who have powdered the annals of the air with their bone dust. They lit a rare rocket for human courage, but to the science of aeronautics they contributed nothing.

4 BIRD-POWER HARNESSED

In spite of the desperate tragedies of the past, a school of thought still exists maintaining that a man can fly a considerable distance under his own power; and a prize is still offered for the first man-powered machine to make a figure-of-eight return flight between two points half a mile apart. Another aspect of bird-power has also been investigated. As late as the eighteenth century serious studies were being made of eagles with a view to harnessing them and getting them to carry a man. This was finally rejected following a report that the heaviest bird known weighed only 100lb. In fact the heaviest

Pride comes before a fall: King Kai Kawus takes off in glory.

flying bird (dismissing the ostrich) is now known to be the bustard, which rarely exceeds a weight of 40lb. The concept of a team of birds carrying a man in a coach is a recurring fable, which was always useful before the days of practical aeronautics in keeping men's eyes on the ultimate objective—what we should now term valuable public relations in maintaining glamour in the romance of flight. It was part of the folk history concerning Alexander the Great (356–323 BC) that he had been borne aloft in his throne carried by four gryphons. Since nobody has yet produced alive or dead the fabulous gryphon, which had an eagle's head and wings with a lion's body, the report may be rejected in favour of the far more circumstantial account of a similar excursion by the ancient Persian King Kai Kawus.

This monarch, who lived in Iran about 1600 BC, was living such a good life and imposing such peace and order on his subjects that the forces of evil took offence. The leader of the fallen angels called a meeting and declared to his fellow devils that, since Kai Kawus was making their lives so difficult, he would have to be persuaded to depart from God, preferably through pride. A plan was hatched and one of the fallen angels, disguised as an attractive young man, met the king while he was out hunting, gave him a bunch of roses as a flower-power preliminary, and began to flatter him. 'Such is your glory and splendour', he said, 'that the vault of heaven should be your throne. The whole earth submits to your will, and all that is missing is that heaven itself should obey you. Why do you not mount into heaven to call the sun and moon to order?' The idea appealed to the king and, on the advice of astrologers, he had his huntsmen raid eagles' nests and capture the eaglets. The young birds were fed on roast meat in captivity. When the eagles were as strong as lions, they were starved while a throne was constructed of reeds reinforced with gold plating. Long lances were fastened to the four corners of the throne, and on top of them were placed quarter-carcasses of succulent roast lamb. The king took his place on the throne with a cup of wine in his hand. The hungry eagles were harnessed to the lances so that they could not quite reach the meat. Unfortunately, since they never did reach their dinner, the eagles finally tired, folded their wings, and deposited the king none too gently in a remote northern forest, from which he was finally rescued by his army, seeking him with elephants.

The first written account of this adventure was included by the poet Abou'lkasim Firdousi in a 60,000-line epic called *Sháhnáma*, the Book of Kings, commissioned in the year AD 976 at the astonishing fee of one gold piece per line. Regrettably, on delivery of the manuscript, the Shah Mahmud Ibn Sabuktagin reneged on the price he had agreed, and paid only 60,000 silver pieces. The indignant Firdousi showed his scorn by giving the messenger who brought this fee a tip of 20,000 pieces, giving 20,000 more to the bath-keeper of the establishment where he received the rebuff, and passing over the last 20,000 to a beer-seller in exchange for one glass of beer—a noble rage that no other aeronautical writer has braced himself to duplicate.

5 BROOMSTICKS AND FLYING SAUCERS

The other stream of fable that kept alive the concept of flight was the elevation of witches. The primary function of witches in all civilisations has been to act as principals in the fertility cult. At a very early age they became endowed in popular imagination with the ability to fly. Flight was not necessarily achieved on broomsticks. Witches in central Africa are said to fly on saucer-shaped winnowing baskets. This is not the first time that circular aircraft have been reported in the fabulous history of flight, for the Emperor Shun of China entrusted himself to the air with the support of round reed hats. But while the Chinese model may well have anticipated

An experienced hag gives a young witch circuits-and-bumps instruction in flying a broomstick.

parachute descent, the African disks are a genuine theoretical forerunner of the modern flying saucer.

Broomsticks for levitation were not at first confined to witches. There is a twelfth-century fresco in the cathedral at Schleswig showing Frija, the genially amorous wife of the chief Germanic god Woden (Odin) flying on a broomstick, naked except for a billowing robe. The aircraft itself was not necessarily a broomstick, as long as it conformed to the general shape. A picture by the sixteenth-century Flemish painter Brueghel the younger shows a witch astride a baker's peel, the long wooden shovel used to remove bread from the oven. Arab witches (and later the New England squadron) could manage even without a tail unit, and flew naked on sticks. But orthodoxy in Europe generally demanded the besom-broom model.

The belief that witches could fly put the thrilling prospect of aerial travel more within the reach of ordinary people than it had ever been before. Under torture, but sometimes more voluntarily, witches not only confessed that they flew—which was 'common knowledge' at the time—but also revealed how they did it. They first rubbed themselves with an ointment. There were three formulae for ointments. Other than grease (which, regrettably, was best if it were baby fat) the operative ingredients were aconite, belladonna and hemlock. These happen to be the three most poisonous plants growing freely in Europe. Aconite brings about a slowing, irregularity, and finally arrest of the heart. Belladonna, in a very small dose—even as few as fourteen berries of deadly nightshade is a fatal intake—produces wild excitement and delirium. Hemlock, though it normally brings on paralysis, may sometimes cause delirium. The unguent was generally applied to the soft skin of the inner thighs and the membranes of the vagina. The absorption of these drugs from an ointment could, some scientists estimate, result in the physiological effects of mental confusion, excitement, dizziness and the irregular action of the heart which (as in the half-dream of falling before dropping off to sleep) can duplicate the sensation of flying.

Self-deceived in group hypnosis, and under the influence of drugs, the seventeenth-century witches in England and America certainly thought they flew to their sabbats. Mary Osgood confessed at Salem, Massachusetts, in 1692 that she had flown on a pole from Andover to Five-Mile-Pond and back. Goody Foster and Martha Carrier admitted to having shared a pole, but, the aircraft being overladen, the pole had broken, and Goody Foster was still bruised and sore from her forced landing. In England witches on trial even disclosed their in-flight jargon. Elizabeth Style, one of the 'Somerset witches' accused in 1664, revealed that the contemporary codewords for 'Scramble' and 'Chocks away' were *Thout, tout a tout, throughout and about*, uttered indifferently as an alert before mounting and a morale-boosting slogan when steady on the broomstick. Alice Duke and Anne Bishop confirmed this and added that the order 'Return to base' was given by a simpler cry of *Rentum tormentum*.

6 AIRBORNE MAN SURVIVES

Aeronautics as exercised by witches, birdmen and tethered eagles were all analysed by worthy John Wilkins, later Bishop of Chester, in a book called *Mathematicall Magick*, which he published in 1648. Witches, spirits and angels were his weakest area, for he was caught between superstition and science. He could avoid discussing the antique abstract of St Thomas Aquinas that a company of angels can dance on the point of a needle; but it was more difficult to be rational about witches. He was a man of his time, brought up amid the psychopathically sick obsession with stripping and hanging witches that King James I, and later the Puritan Parliamentary armies of the Civil War, brought south from Scotland. He was a Cambridge don and later Master of Trinity within the Eastern Counties territory of Matthew Hopkins, the self-styled Witchfinder-General, who amassed a fortune from the execution of hundreds of women in one campaign.

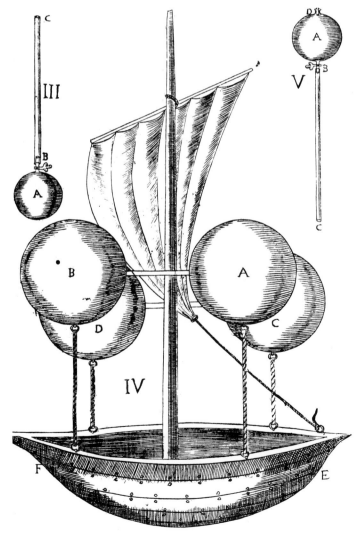

The right idea wrongly executed: Francesco de Lana's proposed flying-boat of 1670. The evacuated copper globes were to be of 20ft diameter. Because of the weight problem the copper could have been no thicker than 1/250in, and the globes would have collapsed under the enormous atmospheric pressure. But the conception started others thinking . . .

But Wilkins became a founder-member of the Royal Society—Samuel Pepys used to have 'noble discourse' with him—and it was the scientific scepticism of the Royal Society from 1660, alongside the moral scepticism of King Charles II, which dramatically eased the lynching and legal condemnation of witches. Sir Matthew Hale, Lord Chief Justice in 1671, discharging an old woman accused of witchcraft, remarked that whether she walked home to freedom or decided to fly through the air was immaterial to the court. 'There is no law against flying', said a judge fifty years later when Jane Wenham, an alleged witch, was accused of doing that.

The examination by Bishop Wilkins of the other methods of flight, which he had classified, were entirely objective. Instances of flying 'by the help of fowls', he declared, were wholly fabulous and fictional. On practical human attempts to fly his comments, pragmatical then, were extremely logical as viewed from the standpoint of more modern science. He saw no reason why birdmen should not experiment with wings, *not from a tower* but by running with them and soaring and sinking until they had got the feel of them, so that by practice they might achieve the facility 'to step constantly ten yards at a time'. In the great sprint to fly of two and a half centuries later this insistence on zealous practice at flight control was heeded only by Otto Lilienthal and the Wright brothers.

Wilkins devoted his most serious consideration to the fourth possibility of 'the art of flying', which he listed as 'by means of a flying chariot'. He declared that a putative flying chariot 'can never be too big or too heavy, if the space which it possesses in the air, and the motive faculty in the instrument [aircraft] be answerable to its weight'. This is a classic simplification (before the conception of any prime-mover steam-engine, not to speak of jet propulsion) of the problem that had to be solved in the two areas of human flight which were eventually developed. It indicated that lighter-than-air 'chariots' were immediately feasible; and that heavier-than-air conveyances were possible once the 'motive faculty' (ie, a mechanically effective engine) could be invented, with a capacity, in the words of the genius who was to follow Wilkins 'to make a surface support a given weight by the application of power to the resistance of air'.

It was in lighter-than-air craft that the next stride of progress was made. In 1670 a Jesuit priest, Francesco de Lana, projected a 'flying-boat' supported in the air by four copper globes entirely evacuated of air, and propelled by a sail. The Italian padre's proposition never materialised, because it demanded metal with an impossible ratio of thickness and strength; but his theoretical thinking was right, and he laid down the principle of lighter-than-air aircraft construction. Almost a century passed, however, before a favourable major development occurred.

This was the isolation of hydrogen by the English millionaire amateur of science Henry Cavendish, in 1766, and the realisation that this was a gas of extreme lightness. A Scottish chemist, Joseph Black—like Cavendish, he was born in France, where the practical application of hydrogen to aeronautics was successfully accomplished—saw that if a bladder could be filled with hydrogen, and the total weight of bladder and gas were less than the weight of the air it displaced, the bladder would rise. He proposed 'merely for amusement' to have a bladder made from the foetal membrane of a calf and to test this idea, but he had just become professor of chemistry at Edinburgh, and in the pressure of work the idea did not seem amusing enough. The experiment was not made until, in 1783, the Academy of Sciences in Paris gave urgent instructions that hydrogen inflation should be speedily pursued on a full-size scale with the object of lifting a man into the sky.

Ironically, the spur that prompted the French Academy to rise to the occasion was the 'invention' of a rival gas that did not really exist, and the technical accident that this 'gas' was capably handled by men whose trade gave them the most useful experience in packaging it. Two brothers, Joseph and Etienne Montgolfier, who ran a papermaking business at Annonay, near Lyon, were interested in the possibility of aerial navigation. They tried to put 'clouds into bags'

Hostile reception for the scientific pioneer: the attack on the first *Charlière* balloon at Gonesse, near Paris, illustrated immediately after the event.

Le ballon ci-dessus étant tombé près de Gonesse, les paysans le prennent pour un monstre d'une espèce nouvel.^{le} tombé du Ciel. Ils l'attaquent à coups de fusil et de fourche et finissent par l'attacher à la queue d'un cheval. Quelques uns s'imaginent que c'est la lune chue sur la terre.

by enclosing steam in paper carriers, and even introduced home-made hydrogen into bags; but on both occasions the bags would not fly, presumably because the paper had become sodden first by the water and then by free sulphuric acid in the vapour. So they turned to a simpler effluent. They observed that smoke from their factory chimney went upwards, and decided to put smoke into the paper bags they were so skilled at making. Their first smoke-filled paper bags went satisfactorily up to the ceiling. They built bigger bags, of silk lined with paper, and eventually they had to go out into the fields. A *ballon* (as they now called the container) of 650cu ft capacity, when filled with smoke from a fire of damped wool and straw, rose 600ft into the air. They continued to build bigger bags. Seven months after the first paper containers had hit the ceiling the brothers Montgolfier announced a public demonstration. A globe of buttoned linen lined with paper, having a 24,000cu ft capacity, was suspended over a fire in the market place at Annonay. When it was released, it rose to a height of 6,000ft and travelled 1 mile 796yd before landing.

The smoke that filled the contraption was given the name of 'Montgolfier's gas'. It took a year or two to show conclusively that the vessel rose because it contained heated air, which was lighter than the atmosphere at ground level. The hot-air balloon, the *Montgolfière*, had been developed. It was then, in June 1783, that the French Academy of Sciences determined to improve on it. Samples taken of 'Montgolfier's gas' showed that it was about half the weight of cool air, but they knew from Cavendish that hydrogen (then mostly called 'Inflammable Air') was only about one-fourteenth the weight of air, and they determined to build a hydrogen balloon. They enlisted the physicist Jacques Charles to devise some method of generating hydrogen on a hitherto unprecedented scale, and entrusted the construction of the envelope to two brothers named Robert, who had specialised in a method of impregnating silk with rubber to make it gas-tight. In the astonishingly short time of 10 weeks the first ever hydrogen balloon, the *Charlière*, was being filled with hydrogen by suspension over a series of leaden boxes containing iron filings over which dilute vitriol (sulphuric acid) was steadily poured.

At dawn on 27 August 1783 the filled balloon, 13ft in diameter, was escorted by a torchlit procession of guards to the Champ de Mars. Awestruck passers-by fell on their knees at the sight of the silent globe passing through the streets. At five in the evening, while a crowd of 300,000 watched, a cannon was fired, the balloon was released, and a deluge of rain drenched the spectators. The *Charlière* soared to 3,000ft before being lost to sight in cloud, but it was estimated (without scientific confirmation) to have reached an incredible height. In the words of a contemporary account:

> It is presumed that it was carried to a height of more than 20,000 feet, when it burst by the reaction of the Inflammable Gaz upon the Atmospheric Air. It fell at three quarters past five near Gonesse, ten miles [actually, 15 miles] from the Field of Mars. The affrighted inhabitants ran together, appalled by the Hellish stench of sulphur, and two monks having assured them it was the skin of a Monstrous Animal, they attacked

it with stones, pitchforks and flails. The Curate of the village was obliged to attend in order to sprinkle it with holy water and remove the fears of his astonished parishioners. At last they tied to the tail of a horse the first Instrument that was ever made for an Experiment in Natural Philosophy, and trained it across the field more than 6000 feet.

Heartened by the primitive bum's rush that had been the fate of their rival, the Montgolfier brothers sped towards their objective of putting a man in the sky. At Versailles three weeks later, before King Louis XVI and the court of France, they sent up a sheep, a cock and a duck in a basket slung below the balloon to see if the rarified air was harmful to life. The balloon descended a mile and a half away with no casualty, save that the sheep had cruelly kicked the cock. The king decorated the Montgolfiers with the Order of Saint Louis and looked around for some men to despatch towards heaven, hopefully offering two criminals who had been condemned to death. But a young man named Pilâtre de Rozier experimented with ascents in a tethered *Montgolfière*, and declared himself ready for free flight. On 21 November 1783, with the Marquis d'Arlandes as fellow-passenger, he ascended from the Bois de Boulogne in a north-west wind and travelled 5½ miles at 300ft in 25 minutes. On the voyage the balloon, not unexpectedly, caught fire, but they doused the flames with a wet sponge. Eleven days later Professor Jacques Charles and the elder of the Robert brothers took off from the Tuileries Gardens. After a 27-mile flight lasting 2 hours Charles descended to drop Robert, who was contributing excess weight, and shot up to 9,000ft so alarmingly fast that he never flew again.

Both types of balloon had now successfully carried crews. Airborne man had survived. Energetic struggles swiftly broke out on three fronts: the rivalry between the *Montgolfière* and the *Charlière* (which was thought to have been early settled in favour of hydrogen, and later helium, but there has been an adventurous revival of hot-air ballooning in the 1970s); the quest to develop a means of propulsion not entirely dependent on the wind; and the consequent research for an efficient method of steering a globular balloon. Methods of propulsion suggested included, yet again, trained eagles, and Joseph Montgolfier's own proposal to open a vent in the envelope on the opposite side to that in which it was intended to travel. He did not offer to solve the problem of keeping a spinning balloon stationary while one found the right vent, or of working up any effective pressure in the emission. But compressed air, steam jets, gunpowder rockets and (hand-driven) airscrews were all advanced as theoretical propellants.

Jean-Pierre Blanchard, however, risked ridicule by attacking propulsion and direction with a rudder and a set of silk-bladed oars fitted to a genuinely boat-shaped gondola. Blanchard has been dismissed too airily by some historians as a minor clown. He was certainly a showman—he made public ascents for money, dropped cats in parachutes, and pioneered ballooning in the United States of America on 9 January 1793. But Léo Valentin was a showman, forced to bottle at his own stunt shows for the money he needed to continue his experiments; and even Captain Scott had (much against his inclination) to exhibit himself at charity dinners for many months before he could collect enough funds to enable him to go and die at the South Pole. Jean-Pierre Blanchard was the first professional aeronaut, because he could not afford amateur status; and he had been an experimental would-be flier before the balloon breakthrough. He had built an amphibious 'flying ship' with a rudder, a canopy sail, and fabric-covered oars two years before the final Montgolfier experiments; and he adapted this apparatus to balloon flight, claiming some success. It was Blanchard who, over Chelsea, London, on 16 October 1784, wore his arms out whirling a six-bladed airscrew from the basket of a *Charlière* while his fellow-passenger toiled equally ineffectively at the oars.

Blanchard, aeronaut extraordinary, again equipped his gondola with oars when he rose from Dover at noon on 7 January 1785 with the intention of crossing the English Channel. He was accompanied by his angel, Dr John Jefferies, a physician from Boston, Massachusetts. Dr. Jefferies, who had agreed to finance the flight to make his own scientific observations, found that he was called to sacrifice more than he had anticipated; for the balloon sprang a leak and lost so much height over the Channel that the navigators had to stop rowing, jettison their oars, discharge all their visible ballast, and finally throw every stitch of clothing into the sea in order to keep themselves out of it. When they thankfully descended into a wood near Calais, Dr Jefferies had not even a notebook in which to record that the first Channel crossing by air was concluded in a state of nudity.

Blanchard's success sparked off the expected sporting rivalry, but this ended in significant tragedy. Pilâtre de Rozier, the first man to ascend into the air, had developed a combination of the *Montgolfière* and the *Charlière*, which he called the *Rozière*. It was an arrangement of a hydrogen bag boosted by a hot-air bag to give better regulated lift and fall. The maker of this death trap was a man called Romaine. The two determined to fly from France to England. On 15 June 1785 they ascended from Boulogne, the inventor stoking his fire vigorously to gain height. They were travelling with the components of one of the world's most dangerous natural explosives, separated only by a skin. A spark from the flue reached the hydrogen, and the balloon exploded. De Rozier and Romaine crashed in their car on rocks off the coast. They were the first of a long line of true aeronauts to die in action.

De Rozier's death condemned the *Montgolfière* and to an appreciable extent damped general enthusiasm for ballooning. But the two attempts on the English Channel recorded in their positive and negative aspects a monumental historic occasion and a severe jolt to military strategic thinking. For the first time a sea and a frontier had been crossed by air. Less than a decade later, in the first year of the French Revolutionary War, the French were using balloons for military observation. One decade after that staff officers were seriously contemplating the use of transport balloons by troops for the Napoleonic invasion of England.

7 FATHER OF AERIAL NAVIGATION

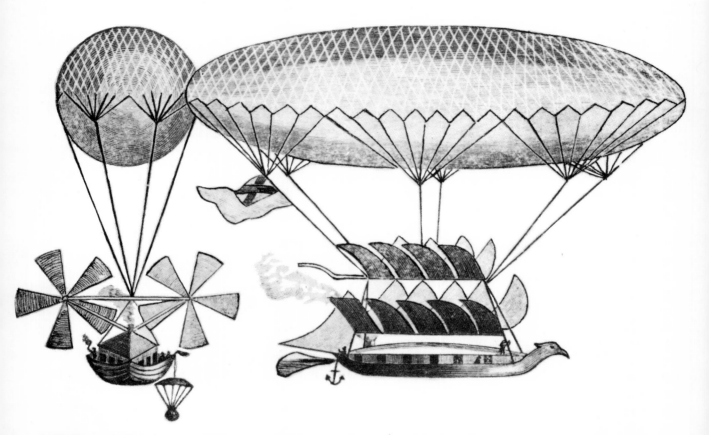

Sir George Cayley's design for an airship, 1817, shows a concession to airscrew propulsion in the head-on view, but a reversion to double-banked bird-wing flappers in the side view.

Maria Edgeworth, the novelist friend of Sir Walter Scott, writing 150 years after the event, said facetiously of Bishop John Wilkins that he had 'prophesied that the time would come when gentlemen, when they were to go a journey, would call for their wings as regularly as they call for their boots'. This satire against aeronauts was somewhat presumptuous, unless it betrays a delicate distaste in a literary person for the rough and tumble of trial and error on aeronautic research within her own domestic circle; for Maria's father, Richard Lovell Edgeworth, had been experimenting since 1786 on a land-based switchback balloon-way system that might have anticipated the railway system by 50 years. Before she turned to writing fiction, Maria had worked closely with her father on mechanics and with him had written the book *Practical Education*. Moreover Maria Edgeworth was an almost exact contemporary of Sir George Cayley, who was designing wings at the very moment she wrote, and has since been confirmed in the title given him in 1846 of Father of Aerial Navigation. But the wings Cayley was working on in 1802

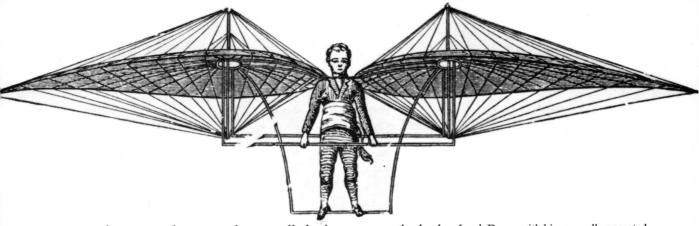

were to sustain a man who was to be propelled—in a manner he had not yet worked out—by a 2hp steam engine, for Cayley had already burst one birdman bubble. 'The attempts to fly by muscular strength have always failed from the time of Daedalus to that of Bishop Wilkins', he said, 'and always must fail when it is considered that the pectoral muscles of a bird exceed seven or eight times in proportional strength the whole power of a man's arms.'

Hence his requirement for a 2hp engine, which he calculated as equalling the strength of 10 men, and could be built, he believed, to weigh less than a man. But at that time he had still to disabuse himself of a further misconception about bird flight: he still believed that birds flew by flapping their wings downwards and backwards, and his engine was intended to work flappers applying this type of thrust.

The subject was highly vulnerable to ridicule, and Cayley was as aware of it as Maria Edgeworth throughout their long lives. When, after 53 years' work, Cayley succeeded in launching a boy in a glider, a correspondent who asked him for technical details displayed the greatest delicacy: 'But excuse the freedom I take, for the bare idea of *flying*, you know, invariably gives rise to jokes.'

Cayley did his best to keep the matter serious, and also to instil among influential people all his powerful optimism. Forty years previously he had written to Viscount Mahon:

> Your Lordship may rest assured that your sanguine expectations of the art of flying, or of aerial navigation as I have chosen to term it, for the sake of giving a little more dignity to a subject rather bordering on the ludicrous in the public's estimation, give great pleasure to one so much interested in this discovery as myself. There can be no doubt of the thing being accomplished. . . . I could make several engines [ie, aircraft] that would mount, with a person to work them, into the air, but the invention will be of no use till conveyance from place to place at great distances from each other can be accomplished with ease either by muscular strength or by the power of some moving engine.

Cayley could indeed give 'dignity' to the concept of man's mastery of the air. He called it a 'noble art' and he endowed it with noble phrasing. 'An uninterrupted navigable ocean that comes to the threshold of every man's door', he said in 1816, 'ought not to be neglected as a source of human gratification and advantage.'

Jacob Degen with his manually operated flapping wings. A similar sketch was sent by Lord Mahon to Sir George Cayley in 1810 and convinced Cayley that flappers were the preferable means of propulsion of airships and aeroplanes.

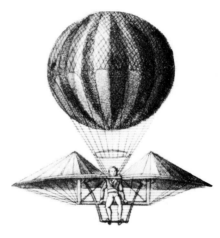

Jacob Degen in his balloon-hopping, wing-flapping kit, 1809. The full diagram shows that Cayley was deceived, and Degen was not fully supported by his wings.

Sir George's shortcomings should also be noted. Although he pioneered and publicised the helicopter, he never gave sufficient importance to the airscrew, although its vertical lift in the helicopter was a most convincing example of its potential. Even when Cayley designed an airship—except for a far-out proposal by General Meusnier in 1785 for a dirigible to be propelled by 80 men turning three airscrews, he was the first to suggest substituting for the spherical balloon the sausage shape, carefully streamlined—Cayley showed in his design a head-on view with airscrews but a side view with flapper propulsion.

Sir George Cayley, of Brompton, Scarborough, Yorkshire, sixth baronet by a creation of Charles II, lived for 83 years between 1793 and 1857, and busied himself with aeronautics, agriculture, architecture, artificial limbs and artillery, to quote only the letter 'A' in his biographical dossier. He invented the hot-air engine and the caterpillar tractor, and in aeronautics alone is credited with 16 'firsts', including the following:

1   Inauguration of the concept of the modern fixed-wing powered aircraft through having separated the system of thrust from that of lift.
2   First use of model gliders for aerodynamic research.
3   Design and construction of the first unpowered man-carrying aeroplanes stabilised laterally by fixed-wing dihedral (ie, a dish-shape in the head-on aspect of the fixed wings) and stabilised longitudinally by an adjustable tail unit and a combined elevator and rudder capable of control.
4   Design and successful construction of the first man-carrying multiplane gliders.
5   The first accurate description of bird flight and the adaptation of flight control by the pilot to match it.

Cayley's preoccupation with flapper wings (even after he had altered their angle of attack to conform with his discovery of the true way in which a bird propels itself) seems to have derived from a curious mental block. In 1809 a Swiss watchmaker named Jacob Degen was reported from Vienna as having 'ascended above the trees in the Prater with artificial wings, taken his flight in various directions, and alighted on the ground with as much ease as a bird'. Cayley fully believed this report, that Degen had mastered some moving-wing machine, and his credulity was bolstered when Viscount Mahon sent him a clear sketch of Degen in his wing harness. What the sketch did not show, because two-thirds of it had been cut out, was that Degen was not 'flying' at all. He was suspended from a balloon that took over half his weight, and he was performing nothing more than pneumatic bounds, or balloon-hopping. Mahon eventually found this out, actually saw the balloon, and told Cayley; but the baronet seemed to want to believe that Degen had really flown, and 36 years later he was still mentioning this feat as a fact. It gave him throughout his life an altogether unreasonable faith in the functional potential of flappers. Even though he had long discarded any reliance on a moving wing for the support of an aeroplane and had accepted fixed wings, he still tended to incorporate separate flappers for propulsion in preference to airscrews.

Cayley should have been convinced by the debacle in 1811 of Albrecht Berblinger, the famous 'Tailor of Ulm', who tried to take off with Degen's wings but without his balloon, and crashed straight into the drink in the Danube.

The melancholy fact that clinched the limitations of Degen's performance was that, like many another aeronautical experimenter, he was heavily in debt, and had been taken to a debtor's prison in Vienna. He arranged the balloon-cum-wings demonstration to raise some money. In order that he should not use the balloon to escape from custody, a rope was tied round his body and held by the jailer, so that he could not jump upwards to a height much more than 50ft. When he had finally paid off his debts in Vienna, Degen moved to Paris. He was badly manhandled by a crowd there when his performance was not considered spectacular enough. Paris was always a dangerous place in which to crash back to the drawing board. The crew of a *Montgolfière* balloon had endured similar rough treatment there when their display had had to be cancelled because of a technical hitch.

Anyone can make today Cayley's original helicopter of 1796. The wing feathers planted in the corks at each end of the spindle are slightly inclined, and the bottom set are 'backwards' in relation to the top. The bow-string is of the same length as the shaft, which Cayley made of whalebone with a hole drilled in the middle to embrace the shaft. The shaft is turned by hand to wind up the string, bending the bow into a spring. When wound, press the helicopter down on a table by a finger held on the top cork, then suddenly release it.

Cayley had had his interest in aeronautics initially sparked at the age of 10, when the Paris balloons had first enabled man to make a true ascent. His first positive achievement was to make a working model aircraft, a re-invention of the helicopter, in 1796. He made it as a practical flying toy, consisting of a vertical spindle with a cork stuck on to either end; horizontally planted in each cork were four wing feathers, 'slightly inclined like the sails of a windmill, but in opposite directions in each set'. The spindle is rotated by a bow-spring (ie, a cord unwound by the tension of a bow that has been drawn taut by previous winding) and the instrument rises to the ceiling.

The helicopter is the earliest form of a practical heavier-than-air flying machine, and was always being re-invented. Traditionally it was first invented by the Chinese, and it was sometimes called the Chinese top. It is illustrated in European manuscripts and paintings from the fourteenth and fifteenth centuries as a fairly bulky hand-held toy. Leonardo da Vinci redesigned it to go by clockwork. The Russian scientist Michael Vasilyevitch Lomonosov made a model with twin contra-rotating rotors in 1754. Jean-Pierre Blanchard constructed (but could not fly) a manually operated man-size helicopter in 1782. Two years later the French naturalist Launoy and his skilled mechanic Bienvenu produced a model helicopter with two contra-rotating helical blades powered by a bow-spring which is so similar to Cayley's that he could have based his 1796 model on it, though he never said so. In 1828 the Italian Vittorio Sarti designed a contra-rotating helicopter and the Englishman David Mayer independently built a man-powered machine, which did not fly. In 1842 W. H. Phillips actually flew a helicopter model powered by steam jets emitted from the rotor tips. Three years later the Englishman Antonio Fidele Cossus proposed a man-sized steam-driven helicopter lifted by a central rotor flanked by two rotors that could be swivelled to send the machine forward and to steer it. This astonishing theoretical anticipation—apart from the power system—had itself been anticipated by Cayley's most controversial and questionable design, when he 'borrowed' another man's idea to design a helicopter that would convert from vertical ascent to forward propulsion (see p. 42).

Cayley was always burning to get men into the air. He spent his life planning, and often building, the structures which, suitably powered, would whisk men to the new world of aerial navigation. Even of his first helicopter he declared that if he had 'a first mover of adequate power'—his constant desideratum of a prime-mover lighter than the steam engine—the spindle, by turning *planes* of a total area of 200 sq ft, would lift a man into the air. He said in 1818 that a feasibility study on the project of a man-carrying helicopter could be carried out for '£3 or £4 expense with the materials I have', and in his last recorded experiment, at the age of 81, he improved his old helicopter into a model with a single three-bladed metal rotor, and sent it 90 ft into the air. 'Mechanical *power*', he was again lamenting, 'within certain limits as to weight, is that which alone is wanting to realise mechanical as well as aerostatic [lighter-than-air] flight on a scale for human use.' But by that time the old man had at least put humans into the air on unpowered gliders.

The power eventually came, yet the helicopter project sagged. Fixed-wing flight, on the surge of Cayley's impetus, moved towards a delayed consummation. There were a few explosive progressions in helicopter technique, but even as late as 1937 the Science Museum in London could print—and could repeat in 1948—its obituary of the helicopter: 'No outstanding success was attained with this type of aircraft, owing chiefly to the large amount of power required and other factors, though in recent years short ascents and some control in the horizontal plane have been accomplished. It is unlikely that the helicopter will for many years be developed to the stage of practical transport.'

They should have told the South-East Asians.

Cayley's design, engraved on a silver disk, of his first aeroplane—a fixed-wing biplane with a kite-form tail unit. The aircraft is propelled by paddles, graphically separating thrust from lift.

9 KITE CLINCHES FIXED WING

In 1799 Sir George Cayley, at the age of 25, engraved a silver disk with the sketch of a flying machine manned by a pilot sitting between the cambered wings of a biplane that has tailplanes and fin in one unit shaped like a paper dart. It is the most significant single design in the whole history of the development of flight, for in one stroke it casts the matrix for future practical aircraft. It has *aeroplanes*, ie, fixed wings, a concept unique at that time, for it concedes that all the effort of past centuries spent in flapping artificial wings in imitation of birds flying (not soaring) is renounced. The problem of *lift* is isolated from preoccupation with thrust, and is tackled by the fixed wings and the angle they make with fluid air. The problem of *thrust* is likewise isolated and passed over to a method of separate propulsion—in this case not a power engine but a pair of broad paddles which the pilot is rowing remotely through levers by pulling on oar-handles. The tail is a separate unit on a universal joint, adjustable by the pilot for steering, and it is of a cruciform kite shape—a tail unit construction that Cayley did not fundamentally change in the 56 years during which he continued to experiment. The radical revolution, from an aeronautical point of view, is that the ornithopter is abandoned and the designer has adopted the aerodynamic principle of the kite.

The kite had been flying for 3,000 years before this new dependence was declared. It was first flown in China, where, among other exercises, it was used as a crafty platform for a fishing line, avoiding the tell-tale shadow of a man or a boat on a lake. It may have been used as a man-carrier then, as it certainly was later. In the West the kite was used in war as early as the fourteenth century, from which date there is an illustration of a kite carrying a bomb being deployed over a besieged city. Benjamin Franklin, experimenting with kites 40 years before his researches into lightning in 1752, used a kite to draw him naked across a lake near Boston. Alexander Wilson, professor of astronomy at Glasgow, put thermometers in kites and flew them in cloud 3,000ft high in 1749.

In Cayley's own time George Pocock was using kites as man-carriers in 1825, and in the next year he developed the most ingenious combination of surface travel and aerial propulsion ever recorded. He attached a complex set of kites to an adapted road-coach and reached extraordinarily sustained speeds. For each kite he designed pairs of cords, like greatly elongated reins, which allowed the surface angle and the lateral movement of the kite to be varied to govern his speed and steering. He built a special light phaeton, very long to keep its stability under speed, and fitted it with a tiller and footbrake. He called it *Le Charvolant*, the Flying Car. On 8 January 1827 he beat the four-horse carriage of the Duke of Gloucester in a straight race, getting his speed up to 22mph over very rough ground, and finding that the kites took part of the weight of the Flying Car over the worst bumps, acting as pneumatic springs.

A kite maintained at the correct angle and pulled forward by a cord in still air will rise, because of an upward thrust of the air. A powered kite is an aeroplane, in the derived sense of the word.

George Pocock's *Le Charvolant*, using kites to draw a horseless carriage at up to 22mph, was a novel demonstration of air power.

Cayley's adoption of the fixed-wing mainplane and kite-shaped tailplane in the first aircraft he designed was a deliberate switch of aeronautical thought to exploit the aerodynamic properties of the steady (not flapping) wing of the soaring bird, and to annex the lift that this configuration supplied for the purpose of sustaining aircraft propelled by a separate means.

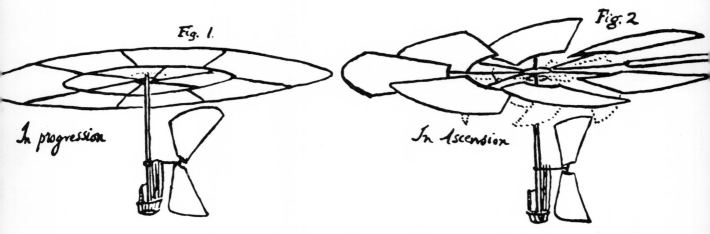

Fig. 1.

In progression

Fig. 2

In Ascension

Robert Taylor's rough sketch, sent to Sir George Cayley, of a machine to combine forward propulsion with vertical ascent. The vanes of the contra-rotating rotors lift the craft as in Fig 2. When the required height is reached the vanes merge into one plane as in Fig 1—'my machine will resemble an immense flat umbrella', said Taylor—and the airscrew pushes the craft forward. The design of the airscrew is based on the new ship's propeller recently introduced by John Ericsson (the screw-propelled *Great Britain* did not make her first Atlantic crossing until 1845). The propeller mechanism is operated from the car in the 'handle' of the umbrella. Taylor believed that the power for his engine would be 'derived from *electro-magnetism* —from which can be obtained from five to ten horse power in the space of an ordinary lady's band box'.

Cayley confirmed his conception of the aerial support given with a fixed wing by building a whirling arm on which to test aerofoils, carefully logging the statistics and performance of model gliders, which he attached to the rig. Then he enjoyed not only the boyish delights but the 'wild surmise' that came from flying them. 'It was very pretty to see it sail down a steep hill', he recorded, 'and it gave the idea that a larger instrument would be a better and a safer conveyance down the Alps than even the surefooted mule.' Cayley began by using an ordinary paper kite for the mainplane, which the wind bellied while sailing; but he was aware of the built-in 'strutted' concave camber of a bird's wing, and shot crows and the occasional heron in order to study this. As an instance of the variety of his work, his 'output' solely directed to putting man in the air may be cited for the two years 1807–9.

He developed an improved hot-air engine to replace the bulky steam engine, and constructed as an alternative a gunpowder engine. He built two ornithopters, finally solved the secret of the technique of bird flight, and (with an occasional sentimental lapse) thereupon largely abandoned the pure flapping-wing machine. He designed the tension wheel—later called the cycle wheel, which avoided the splintering or distortion of the rim by shock transferred through rigid spokes—which was adapted for all aircraft undercarriages, and he did this deliberately for the purpose of aircraft undercarriages, 'thinking how to construct the lightest possible wheel for aerial navigation cars'. He worked out a system of tubular beam construction to incorporate optimum lightness of weight in airframes. He exhaustively researched streamlining, basing his designs for a 'solid of least resistance' on the body shape of a trout, then of a dolphin, and finally of a woodcock. He wrote and had published a profoundly influential essay 'On Aerial Navigation', which laid down the basic aerodynamic theory of all heavier-than-air flight and the requisites for stability and control—in his view dihedral setting of the wings,

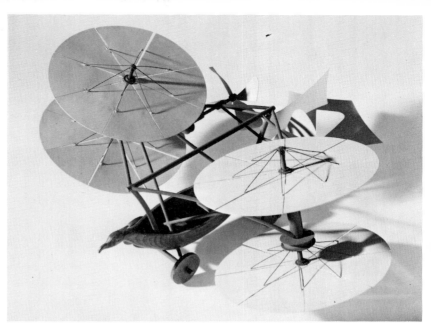

The finished design for a twin helicopter, subsequently propelled by twin airscrews, which Sir George Cayley claimed to have invented. The rotor blades of the dihedrally-set (ie, V-inclined) disk wings are, at flying altitude, mechanically closed to form planes—'like a very flat umbrella', wrote Cayley, repeating Taylor's original words. Twin airscrews of the same shape as Taylor's (which could not have been projected before Ericsson's work was published in 1839) push the aircraft forwards. The car is 'pure Cayley'.

'vertical and horizontal rudders' [ie, rudders and elevators and kite-form tail units]. Moreover he built a full-size glider that was not only intended to carry a man but did on occasion do so, though not with the potential (or the witness) to establish any aeronautical record. Cayley noted at the time: 'When any person ran forward in it, with his full speed, taking advantage of a gentle breeze in front, it would bear upward so strongly as scarcely to allow him to touch the ground; and would frequently lift him up, and convey him several yards together.' This was happening 90 years before the hang-gliding done on the Lilienthal, Chanute and Wright machines, and nearly a century before mechanical man-carrying flight.

There is no record at all of any aeronautical activity or theoretical writing by Sir George Cayley between the years 1818 and 1836. Since he was so evidently and fervently busy for the double decades before and after this gap, it seems that there must be archives still to be discovered, and that a mine of further inspiration may be exploited when such missing papers are found. The bustling energy chronicled after the resumption of the records includes a fresh call to 'the efficient mechanics of this engineering age' to solve 'perhaps the most difficult triumph of mechanical skill over the elements man has had to deal with—I mean the application of aerial navigation to the purpose of voluntary conveyance'. Backing his words with action, he founded in 1839 the Polytechnic Institution in Regent Street, London. Then, in 1842, there began a regrettably unsavoury sequence in his professional life.

A young man from America sailed into Liverpool and at once wrote to Cayley, introducing himself as Robert B. Taylor, and stating that his father had been a doctor in Bolton before emigrating to America in 1819. Taylor said that he had 'imbibed' from his father, who had known Cayley and had often praised his devotion to flying, 'a firm conviction of the practicability of travelling thro' the air by mechanical means, without inflation'.

Robert Taylor then freely outlined a strikingly novel idea, and he enclosed a rough sketch of a machine incorporating this invention, the design of which he intended to patent in the United States. The proposal was for a machine that would ascend as a helicopter by the power of two contra-rotating rotors revolving about the same axis as a double hollow perpendicular shaft. The rotor blades were to be built as vanes, which, once the necessary height had been gained, would close and lock into a flat disk—in effect, a circular mainplane. A pusher propeller would then be operated for forward flight.

Taylor showed that he had not only understood what Cayley had been teaching since 1809—that the concise problem was 'to make a surface support a given weight by the application of power to the resistance of air'—but he had also gone logically beyond that. 'The lateral movement of a large plane surface edgewise, to attain and retain altitude, is, I conceive, your original invention or idea. . . . The rotary ascensive action could be dispensed with if sufficient speed were attained by the rotary propulsive action, with a general angle of the whole machine as in Fig. 1; but to start from the ground requires a perpendicular ascent at first, and I consequently screw the plane up as in Fig. 2.' (This is a deliciously graphic Americanism which deserved a longer life, but the existence of this letter did not become public knowledge until 1961, by which time even our trainee pilots were mainly in the jet age.)

Taylor had written this letter to enquire 'whether I have been anticipated in the principle [sic] ideas' and to ask if he might visit Cayley. Cayley replied speedily that he had himself anticipated Taylor, but he would be glad to meet him and 'arrange matters so as to be fair to each'. He wrote: 'Long ago I came to the same conclusion as you have done, as to the main features of the mechanical aerial locomotive; that is, the first rise to be made by two opposite revolving oblique vanes, which should when required become simple inclined planes, or a part of them, for progressive motion by any other propelling apparatus.' But, said Cayley, he had laid the project aside to work for 30 years on developing an engine of sufficiently light weight.

Cayley's assertion that he had a prior claim on this invention must be accounted as either a deliberate untruth or the self-deception of a man 68 years old. There is no evidence on record that Cayley had previously suggested any means of strictly horizontal propulsion—certainly not by the use of an airscrew—as an auxiliary to his 1796 helicopter, though he had referred to the helicopter several times in later papers.

Cayley's subsequent behaviour is even more questionable. He first privately checked that Robert Taylor had not taken out a British patent for his idea, and then coolly announced that he had invented a similar machine himself. With his superior experience he produced a much more impressive design, but it must still be deemed a straight theft. For reasons that may or may not have any connection with this action, nothing more was ever heard of Robert Taylor. The American eagle had made a first strike at the principle of mechanical flight, and the entrenched establishment had beaten him back.

11 AERIAL STEAM CARRIAGES

Throughout the 60-year marathon of Cayley's active life in aeronautics there was no comparable genius to keep up with him, and fewer than half a dozen bright young men who could pace him for a lap or two. In 1831 Thomas Walker published a design for a tandem monoplane that at least acknowledged the force of Cayley's propaganda for the fixed-wing concept, but also capitulated to his abiding weakness—the obsession with flapper-propulsion. Walker's dream machine had no hope of flying, but it grabbed a disproportionate influence on aircraft design. The tandem format was taken up 40 years later by D. S. Brown, a member of the Aeronautical Society, who published an account of his experiments with this system of achieving longitudinal stability. The publication had an influential circulation. It may have played a part in Lawrence Hargrave's invention of the box-kite in 1893. It certainly influenced Samuel Pierpoint Langley, the secretary of the Smithsonian Institution in Washington, who was commissioned by President McKinley to build an aircraft for the United States Army, and produced his *Aerodrome A* in 1903. Langley in his turn influenced 'Professor' John J. Montgomery of California and the venturesome Louis Blériot—a dashing pilot, but perhaps too dashing to make a top-rate designer.

When Sir George Cayley pronounced, in 1809, that through the 'noble art' of aerial navigation 'we shall be able to transport ourselves and families, and their goods and chattels . . . with a velocity of from 20 to 100 miles per hour', the time was not ripe for him to be taken seriously by the public. The smoothest and most reliable comparable transport was by water, on the new canals. But then the railway era dawned. Between 1825 and 1837 93 Acts of Parliament authorised the construction of 1,500 miles of railroad, and public opinion was stirred to appreciate the possibilities of a new mechanical age. Consequently, when a fresh missionary advocated an even more fantastic mode of transport, he was taken far more seriously by the popular mind (led by newspaper reference and middle-class gossip), in spite of the irrepressible tendency of the intellectuals and the professional comics to ridicule him.

Cayley, with all his technically backed prophecy, never achieved the impact registered by William Samuel Henson when, on 24 March 1843, Mr J. A. Roebuck, Member of Parliament for Bath, moved in the House of Commons for leave to introduce a Bill for an Act of Incorporation of Henson's Aerial Transport Company, which was to operate an Aerial Steam Carriage to convey passengers, goods and mail through the air. Four days later a patent was granted protecting this Locomotive Apparatus. Within three days more the *Mechanics Magazine* published the full specifications. With the most skilfully organised publicity, a sheaf of very finely executed illustrations was distributed, showing the Aerial Steam Carriage flying over London,

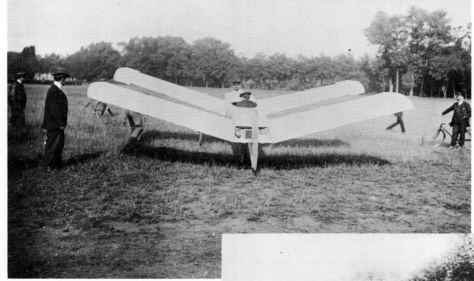

Thomas Walker's proposed tandem monoplane was designed to have inherent stability, countering fore-and-aft pitching, by the disposition of the plane surfaces in the rear. It never flew. but it inspired a number of successors, including S. P. Langley's Aerodrome A, seen on its launching catapult-rig in the Potomac river before a (disastrous) take-off in 1903 . . .

. . . and Blériot's No VI *Libellule* (Dragonfly), which hopped 150m in 1907.

The only pure derivative that did fly, and looked remarkably like the original Walker, was John J. Montgomery's glider, which the professional parachute-jumper D. Maloney launched from a hot-air balloon in California in 1905. Maloney made two hazardous landings, but on the third launch he crashed and was killed.

Paris, the Pyramids, India and China. The choice of the eastern landfalls was very pointed, since Henson was simultaneously soliciting investment from the public in the promotion of a company that would run the Aerial Steam Carriage in fleets 'to convey Passengers, Troops and Government Despatches to China and India in a few days'. The conception of transporting troops by air, put forward a century before it was actually consummated, was a master-stroke of promotion in those imperial days.

The aircraft it was proposed to use for this great venture had not been built, let alone tested, but it was described in very great detail. Henson was not a fraudulent bucket-shop operator, though he was afterwards represented as such. He was an enthusiastic but not entirely profound inventor, then aged 38. He had settled in Chard, Somerset, where he ran a lace factory. He had registered solid inventions during the previous eight years for lace machinery and an improved steam engine, and later, possibly in disgust at the reception of his Aerial Steam Carriage, or as a determined effort to avoid impetuous suicide, he invented an improved safety razor. He had turned to aeronautics after 1838. His aircraft design was influenced by Cayley—it would have been retrogressive if it had ignored him— but Henson introduced original features.

Ariel, the Aerial Steamer, or the Aerial Steam Carriage, as it was variously called, was a monoplane with rectilinear wings of 150ft span and 30ft chord that were covered with oiled silk. The wings made a single plane, without dihedral setting, and were cambered and double-surfaced (a feature not always shown in 'artists' impressions'). They were ribbed, and braced with wires tautened by kingposts. A fan-shaped tailplane could be diminished in spread—its maximum area was one-third of the mainplane—and it was moved up or down from a pivot to work as an elevator. A vertical sail beneath the tail acted as a rudder. A 25–30hp steam engine of special efficiency and lightness, housed in the fuselage, worked two six-bladed pusher airscrews mounted behind the mainplane. There was a tricycle undercarriage fitted with Cayley's tension wheels. Because the power of the engine was calculated to be sufficient only to maintain the Aerial Steamer in level flight, it was intended from the first that the aeroplane should take off downhill. The gross weight was 3,000lb, the engine taking up 600lb of this, so that the passenger list of this troopship could hardly have comprised even a platoon—half a dozen armed and accoutred men at most.

Sir George Cayley, within a week of the publication of the full patent specifications of the Aerial Steam Carriage, criticised Henson's machine severely in print on account of its size, its lack of provision of lateral stability, the impracticable demand that it should take off downhill, and the low rating of the engine. Cayley had always shown himself timid in the use of large wings, particularly mainplanes with a high aspect ratio [ie, wide span and comparatively narrow, like a heron's wing] and he forecast that the Aerial Steam Carriage would break up in flight. He made a suggestion as an alternative that was to have a profound effect on design: 'If, therefore, so large a surface be contemplated for trying this experiment, would it not be more likely to answer the purpose to compact it into the form of a *three decker*, each deck being 8 or 10 feet from the other, to give free room for the passage of the air between them?'

It was 65 years before a mechanically powered triplane was actually flown, though Cayley himself was building successful triplane gliders in his last great spurt of research. But his apparently rather casual remark (when it was belatedly appreciated) laid the foundation of the thinking of all the first biplane designers, particularly the work of Octave Chanute, which greatly influenced the shape of the successful Wright biplanes. Cayley completed this paper in the *Mechanics Magazine* of 8 April 1843 by moving away from criticism of Henson and modestly announcing that he had solved the problem of heavier-than-air flight, 'combining all the requisite principles of action' in the realisation of the helicopter-pusher aircraft, purloined from Robert Taylor, which has already been mentioned.

As far as the flying troopship was concerned, there were other constructive professional criticisms, accompanied naturally by a flood of amateur facetiousness, not unmixed with a romantic yearning for the fulfilment of this fantastic idea. Nevertheless, easy as it was to ridicule this drawing-board project, Henson's Aerial Steam Carriage not only incorporated all the aeronautical 'musts' (except dihedral wings: ailerons were not yet invented) that had accumulated since the noble art was taken at all seriously, but also minted a reliable standard design, which most of the earliest monoplane aircraft in the twentieth century were to adopt. Beyond this, it achieved public acceptance, both as a credible assurance that the Aeroplane Age was no dream but a not-too-distant era, and as a credible representation of what the future Aerial Locomotive would look like. Pictures of the Steamer were popular ornaments throughout the Victorian period.

However, the Aerial Transit Company was never formed. Its over-slick promotion and the pseudo-scientific opposition to it lost it all credibility with investors, and they shied away from supporting it. Henson did not make his quick fortune, but—and it is an indication that, aeronautically speaking, his heart was in the right place—he decided to build and test a model since he had not acquired the funds to build an aeroplane.

The Aerial Steam Carriage, the aircraft that never was but which crystallised in Victorian hearts the conviction that man would fly in their lifetime. This influential phantom, illustrated in magazines all over the world, did more to condition stolid humanity that it was no longer earthbound than any nicely calculated hypothesis of the devoted thinkers who made the achievement possible. Ariel had cambered wings measuring 150ft by 30ft, a mobile tailplane working as elevator, and a 25hp steam engine operating two six-bladed pusher airscrews. The tricycle under-carriage was fitted with Cayley's tension wheels. The payload was light, possibly 1,000lb.

12 NECKS MUST BE BROKEN

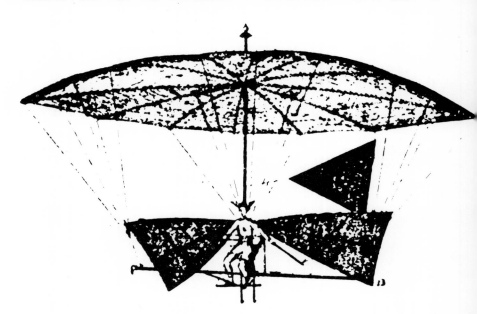

'A hundred necks have to be broken', warned Sir George Cayley, and this machine caused the first. François Letur had made several successful gliding descents from a balloon in this canopy-wing glider with additional flappers. He gave a display at the Cremorne Gardens—Cayley had also declared that there was no money to be made out of aeronautics except from fairground exhibitions. He was trying to right a defect in the balloon when the wind dashed him against some trees. He died of his injuries a week later, in July 1854.

With his friend John Stringfellow, an engineer who was also in the lace industry at Chard, W. S. Henson built a model of *Ariel* with a 20ft wing-span and an ingenious little steam engine refined by Stringfellow. Before the tests were complete, the money ran out. At this stage, three years after the moral collapse of the Aerial Steam Carriage, Henson wrote to Sir George Cayley asking for aid:

> You probably imagined that I had long since given it up as a failure, and you will no doubt be pleased to hear that I have, in conjunction with my friend Mr Stringfellow, been [working] more or less ever since 1843 towards the accomplishment of Aerial Navigation, and that we feel very sanguine as to the result of our endeavour and consider that we have

Stringfellow's triplane, following the suggestion of Cayley, which was exhibited in 1868, and had a powerful influence on future design.

Stringfellow's fresh design of a steam-powered model based on Henson's Aerial Steamer, demonstrated in 1848 and flown off an overhead wire, was for long thought to have made the first genuine mechanical flight in history.

arrived at that stage of proceedings which justifies us in obtaining that pecuniary assistance necessary to carry on our efforts upon an enlarged scale and with increased energy. We therefore resolved to apply to you as the Father of Aerial Navigation to ascertain whether you would like to have anything to do in the matter or not.

It is perhaps a little disconcerting to realise that the reason why Cayley was given the title of Father of Aerial Navigation, which everyone since has confirmed rather than challenged, was because he was being addressed by a man who wanted some money from him. But there is no reason to believe that Henson was just flattering him.

In any case the ploy did not work. In a kind but firm letter—very fatherly, indeed—Cayley encouraged Henson, and invited him to London to demonstrate 'any experimental proof of mechanical flight maintainable for a sufficient time by mechanical power'. He ended his letter with a moving and dignified acceptance of the ugly truth that many aeronautical inventors have had to stomach—that their best hope for support depends on their value as a circus attraction, and that this value is enhanced by the occurrence of death in their aeronautical sphere and the likelihood of the death of the enthusiast himself. Yet these deaths might be necessary:

> Though I have not any weight of capital to apply to such matters, I perhaps might be able to aid you in some manner by my experience in connection with other mechanical persons. I do not however think that any *money*, excepting by exhibition of a novelty, can be made by it. A hundred necks have to be broken before all the sources of accident can be ascertained and guarded against.

Henson continued for a little time to experiment with his model, unsupported by Cayley or other 'mechanical persons' except String-

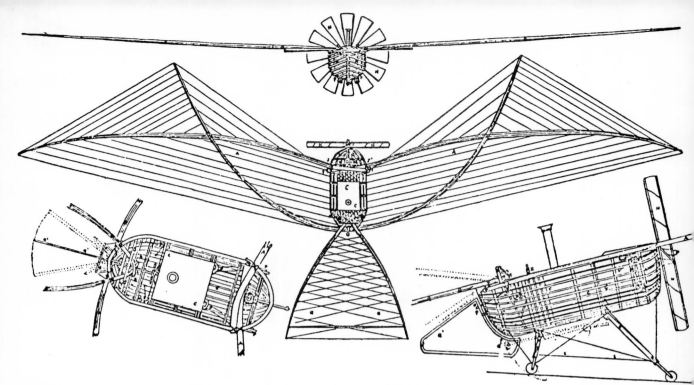

In 1857 Félix du Temple flew the first powered model aircraft to take off under its own steam (literally) and land without damage. Immediately he registered a patent for this beautifully designed full-size aircraft.

fellow, but he lost heart, left Chard, married, and in 1849 emigrated to America. Stringfellow remained. He redesigned Henson's model with a tiny steam engine driving four-bladed pusher propellers, and demonstrated it in an empty factory building in Chard and at the Cremorne Gardens in Chelsea—the showman's exhibition that Cayley had prophesied they must accept. The working model aircraft was launched from an overhead wire in the correct attitude of flight. For many years it was said that it genuinely flew, and that this was therefore the first instance of mechanical flight (with an unmanned model) in history. This claim is no longer believed. In any case Stringfellow made no money from the exploit, and decided to cut his losses. He, too, went to the United States, but he returned: 20 years later, in 1868, when he was almost 70, Stringfellow exhibited at the historic first exhibition of the Aeronautical Society a model steam-powered triplane resolving the main criticism by Cayley in 1843 of the Aerial Steam Carriage with which he had been connected. This model, which also did not fly, again caught the public imagination by its appearance as the older Ariel had once done; and because it was often illustrated, it kept the multiplane structure within the vision of the designers, and led to the shape of the first practical biplane.

The first powered model aircraft to fly was the graceful monoplane designed by the 34-year-old French naval officer Félix du Temple, working with his brother Louis. Powered by steam operating one 12-bladed tractor airscrew, it took off from the ground under its own power and landed without damage. Encouraged by this success, du Temple patented a full-size aeroplane, but he was not able to build it for many years. However, in 1874, the machine was constructed and tested with a pilot. Powered with a hot-air engine, it was launched (down a ramp) and it took off successfully—the first powered

A reconstructed model (made for the
Qantas History of Flight collection) of
du Temple's full-size powered aircraft of
1874, the first to take off carrying a man.
It had a retractable tricycle undercarriage.
The wingspan was 117ft 8in, the length
53ft 5in.

man-carrying aircraft to do so. But it cannot be said to have flown under control.

Over the same period another French sailor, Captain Jean-Marie Le Bris, was designing, occasionally flying, and inevitably crashing, a full-size glider of parachute design. This seems to have been the last practical glider to carry its man in a boat-shaped cradle corresponding to the airship gondola or Cayley's car. Its wings were modelled on the albatross, a bird Captain Le Bris had studied on voyages in southern seas. He was also enterprising in using a moving cart from which to launch himself. He made one successful glide, but crashed after a second take-off and broke a leg. He made another machine with which he conducted many practical experiments, mainly in ballast. He finally saw it destroyed in a serious accident. But Le Bris had set a good standard for detailed experimentation with full-size machines.

Sir George Cayley died in the year du Temple and Le Bris notched their own first gratifying successes. Cayley had never got as far as installing his hot-air engine in even a model aircraft, like du Temple, or experiencing the fearful personal test of preliminary flight control, like Le Bris. But he did put a man into the air on an aeroplane and, as an old man in his eighties, there was excuse enough for him that he could not himself make the ascent. The Marquis de Bacqueville, consumed with ambition to wing-flap across the Seine, felt cold feet and asked his valet to put on the wings. Cayley, with none of his endurance or keenness of observation surviving to take him gliding, requested his coachman to go in his place. But he met with a parallel mutinous response.

Cayley had sent a boy for a few feet into the air in 1849, but not in free flight. He used a full-size aeroplane, designed as the triplane

51

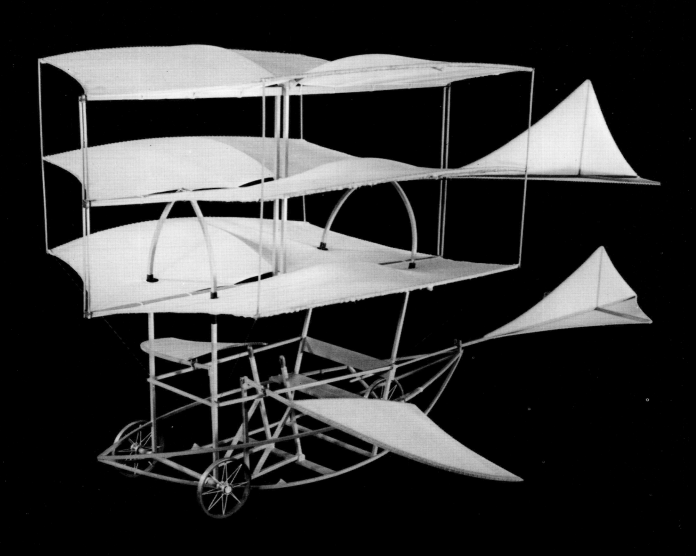

Le Bris' second albatross-winged glider, seen on its launching cart. It crashed in 1868.

he had recommended at the time of the Henson controversy six years earlier. He was at the same time very preoccupied with developing the hot-air engine, but he did not install it in the glider. Instead he fitted the car with flappers with which the pilot was supposed to row to glory. Glory of a sort did come. Cayley recorded: 'A boy of about ten years of age was floated off the ground for several yards on descending the hill, and also for about the same space by some persons pulling the apparatus against a very slight breeze by a rope.'

In 1853, using another full-size machine, which he called his New Flyer, Cayley and his ground crew moved on to the east side of the deep dale behind Brompton Hall, his country home. He requested his coachman to occupy the car, which was equipped with handles to work flappers and levers to brake the undercarriage wheels. The machine was hustled down the hill until it was launched into the air. It sailed across the valley, well stabilised because of Cayley's previous trimming of the craft, and not immediately put out of kilter by the coachman's frenzied manipulation of the flappers. It landed, after a flight of some 500yd, not so neatly as might have been hoped, hitting the opposite side of the dale and overturning the car. The ground crew rushed across to free the coachman from the debris, but old Cayley, knowing he was not spry enough to keep up with them, took his time. Consequently the coachman, once he had been set solidly on his feet, had to cup his hands to shout across the valley his reaction to this historic occasion. The bellowed message was: 'Please, Sir George, I wish to give notice. I was hired to drive, and not to fly.'

Four and a half years later Cayley was dead, having spent the interim designing an even more complex machine than any he had yet suggested. With the exception of the provision of an adequate engine, the key to almost all the aeronautical problems that presented themselves between his death and the Wrights' triumph was tucked, not too obscurely, within the records and statements of his work. But he was forgotten almost immediately. For the next 50 years individual inventors were pecking away at problems he had already largely investigated and solved.

Qantas reconstruction of Cayley's 'boy carrier', or Old Flyer, the triplane in which he floated a ten-year-old off the ground in 1849, the first time a human being had left the ground in a heavier-than-air machine. The wing-span was 10ft, overall length and height 20ft.

13 THE STRUGGLE FOR POWER

Stringfellow's improved design of a powered monoplane based on Henson's Aerial Steamer had used a delicate steam engine to drive its pusher propellers, and that had at least moved the model forward through the air, even if the aircraft could not strictly be said to have flown. Félix du Temple had substituted steam for clockwork in the successful model that is accepted as having flown in 1858. In the interval between these two small-scale achievements a steam engine had been used for practical flight, though not on a heavier-than-air machine. Henri Giffard, who had made a very fast fortune from his invention of the steam injector, devoted himself to experimental work on ultra-light steam engines. In 1852, when he was 27 years old, he installed a 3hp engine weighing 350lb in a car cannily suspended 20ft below the envelope of an airship 143ft long, which was inflated with coal gas. The engine, driving an 11ft diameter airscrew at 110rpm, coaxed the airship for 17 miles at a speed of up to 5mph, but was not powerful enough to turn the craft in a circle or push it back to base.

It was a demonstration that steam propulsion of man-carrying aircraft was possible, but it showed equally decisively that the problem of the great weight demanded by the engine of the day had still to be overcome. Twenty years after Giffard's first flight the prospect of a positive outcome in the struggle for power seemed even to have deteriorated. An airship designed by Dupuy de Lôme, greatly improved in the construction of its envelope, managed to achieve only the same speed as Giffard's craft, but the four-bladed propeller was worked manually by eight men. They must have registered corporatively four times the weight of the steam engine, a statistic marking no great step towards supersonic speed. However, at the end of the same year, 1872, the German engineer Paul Haenlein fitted a Lenoir-type gas engine beneath an airship envelope inflated with coal gas, and ingeniously ran a pipe from the gas bag to supply fuel for the engine. With the four cylinders of the gas engine driving two airscrews at 40rpm, he reached a declared speed of 10mph. But the fact that he had little directional control on his first flight, and that he contributed nothing to the record books as the result of any other flight, indicates a crop of snags that he did not care to particularise to a waiting world.

Designers of heavier-than-air craft inwardly digested the obvious moral. In addition to steam engines they installed model power units utilising clockwork, compressed air, gunpowder and twisted rubber—the last a valid medium of propulsion, as all boys have known for a century, but, from the point of view of efficiency, a method that often demands more work in storing the energy than the rapture attained in releasing it. For full-scale aircraft they called additionally on human pedal-power, the burning of alcohol to fire a boiler, and the explosion of ether in eight chambers to rotate a gas turbine. As late

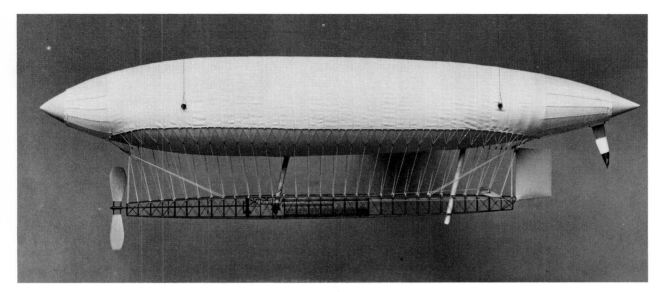

A rare achievement for electric storage batteries. The streamlined airship *La France*, powered by a 9hp electric motor drawing current from chromium chloride batteries, developed power enough in 1884 to reach a speed of 14½mph and to turn and reach base. The tractor propeller is at the bow of the 108ft bamboo car.

as 1906 the dainty Vuia monoplane, which was important for other reasons, flew—or rather, hopped—on carbonic acid gas. In 1877 and 1878 two separate French inventors lightened the engine weight of the helicopters they were building by keeping most of the power-producing apparatus on the ground and running the propulsive fluid—in one case steam and in the other compressed air—into the aircraft from a hose, a method that severely limited the operating ceiling of the helicopters. Just after that outburst of eccentricity the Russian Nikolai Kibalchitch made a proposal that he should build a rocket-propelled aircraft using one swivelling jet for vertical ascent and forward flight; but since he was at the time under sentence of death for having assassinated the Czar Alexander II with a bomb blast, the idea may have been put forward merely to gain time until he should have finished his project—like the condemned man in the classic story who was asked if he had any last request before his execution, and put up the modest proposal that he should be allowed to learn the violin.

Designers of lighter-than-air craft went on to dabble with electric power derived from storage batteries, and they achieved a certain success. In 1884 the French engineers Charles Renard and A. C. Krebs built the streamlined airship *La France*, which was longer than Giffard's craft but required only three-quarters of the volume of gas to carry its 4,000lb gross weight, and powered it by a Gramme 9hp electric motor deriving current from comparatively light chromium chloride batteries that Renard had developed. The power unit weighed only 210lb, a remarkable ratio of some 2½lb per hp. A broad tractor propeller 20ft in diameter, fixed at the very front of the 108ft-long bamboo car, pulled the airship at up to 14½mph and allowed a circular

Henri Giffard put the steam engine into the air when he installed a 3hp engine in the car of an airship in 1852. He achieved a speed of 5mph, but had not sufficient power to turn the craft against the weather. The engine was placed well below the boom to which the sail rudder was fixed because the envelope was inflated with combustible coal gas.

course and the return to base. The most telling objection to the propulsion principle—one equally applicable for almost a century to electric motor cars—was that the power system allowed only short flights with minimum payload because of the constant need to replenish the batteries.

Struggle as the designers might, the future power unit for many decades of aerial travel was to be the internal combustion engine, which had already been tentatively installed in Paul Haenlein's airship of 1872. Understandably, its potential for heavier-than-air craft was not immediately accepted, and indeed it had not the requisite neatness, power or reliability until the development of the motor car after 1884.

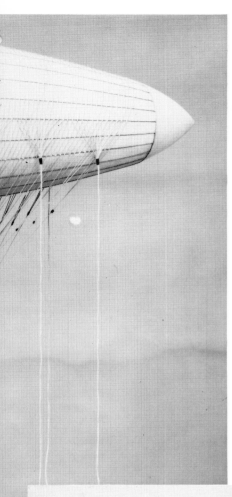

Internal combustion merely refers to the fact that burning something to release its energy in order to power an engine takes place *inside* the cylinder, down which a piston is driven. An external boiler and steam chamber, or their equivalent, is eliminated. Theoretically, one can use anything combustible, even gunpowder.

The references to gunpowder already made may be expanded. In 1870 Gustave Trouvé actually made a model ornithopter fly for 60m, after a mid-air launch, by the action of 12 blank cartridges automatically fired into a Bourdon tube [a coiled metallic tube which tends to straighten out when pressure is exerted within it, and to spring back into coil afterwards]. The straightening of the tube flapped down the wings and the relaxation of the tube at the end of

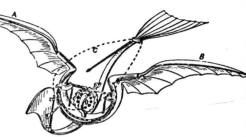

The Vuia monoplane, which was bouncing about the fields near Paris in 1906 and 1907, was the last notable aeroplane to be powered by a carbonic acid motor—in this case made by Serpollet, who had a reputation for steam engines. Lilienthal had installed two carbonic acid gas motors in glider-cum-ornithopter machines in 1893 and later in 1895, but had not tested them in 1896, at the time when he stalled his 'pure' glider No 11 and crashed, and subsequently died. The Vuia aircraft was far more important as being the world's first full-size conventionally shaped monoplane—influencing many contemporary designers—and it was also the first machine in Europe with pneumatically tyred wheels. The carbonic acid motor did work, up to a point. The machine made several recorded hops, the longest being 24m.

Powered by blank revolver cartridges, Gustave Trouvé's model ornithopter flew 60m in 1870, the wings being flapped by the action of the pistol shots straightening out Bourdon tubes.

the explosion brought the wings up, while the next cartridge slipped into place for another shot. In 1885 Enrico Forlanini, the Italian pioneer who built a practical (model) helicopter, tried to propel a model fixed-wing aeroplane by the reaction of gunpowder exploded in a tube. The rocket aircraft proposed by Kibalchitch in 1881 would also have worked by gunpowder, a medium in which the terrorist was something of an export.

Hydrogen was the first 'packageable' combustible gas, and in 1804 Isaac de Rivaz built a hydrogen internal combustion engine in Switzerland. In 1862 Etienne Lenoir, working in France, used an explosive mixture of coal gas and air fired by the recently invented Ruhmkorff induction coil when he adapted a double-action steam engine into a two-stroke gas engine. It showed only 4 per cent efficiency in its conversion of fuel into energy, but the engine was smooth and durable and was much used industrially for low-power work such as pumping and printing. Lenoir tried to apply it both to carriages and boats. In 1865 the Viennese Siegfried Marcus did fit to a hand-cart a two-cycle internal combustion engine exploding benzene vapour by an electric spark, and in 1874 he built a motor car with a single-cylinder 1,570cc four-stroke engine fired by a low-tension magneto. But this engine developed only $\frac{3}{4}$hp, which, permitting a speed of 4mph, offered Marcus the edge on casual promenaders but only the dust and droppings from every carriage horse. The practical internal combustion engine for the automobile and for aircraft was 10 years away in the future, dependent on the development of strong light metals, the mechanical ability to work them, and a number of other factors that were introduced in the 1880s—notably ballbearings, the application of mineral oil, and the exploitation of petroleum spirit.

The pioneers of the work-horse automobile engine, which was adopted as the initial aircraft engine, were Gottfried Daimler and Karl Benz, both working entirely separately in Germany but both producing their brainchild in the same year, 1885. Daimler was a

Pioneer instance of the reduction of the internal combustion engine to portable proportions and thus towards mobility for transport: Siegfried Marcus's second motor car, made in Vienna in 1874, long before Benz and Daimler had applied themselves to the problem, which achieved 4mph with a $\frac{3}{4}$hp petrol-driven engine.

skilled engineer who, after valuable experience of steam engines with the Manchester toolmaking firm of Whitworths, joined Dr N. A. Otto in Deutz, Cologne, to develop Otto's slow-speed stationary gas engines. Working with Otto and his partner Eugen Langen, Daimler was the technical director when the firm produced the then revolutionary four-cycle engine in which the ignition was provided by an open gas-jet briefly exposed to the explosive mixture. But Daimler was concerned to build a light, and therefore portable, gas engine that should run at high speed and use a gas that could be vaporised from a liquid. Because he could not persuade Otto to explore this line of research, Daimler left the firm, taking with him his assistant

Wilhelm Maybach, and set up his own organisation at Cannstadt, near Stuttgart, in 1882.

Next year he devised his own light gas engine with a speed so high—750rpm—that he could use the heat it generated to ignite the explosive mixture. He later added a bunsen burner for each cylinder, to keep the tube incandescent—the famous (and troublesome) 'tube ignition' of the early automobile engines. The fuel Daimler was using was benzene, a hydrocarbon then produced in the distillation of coal tar, fed into a carburettor through which air was introduced from below to bubble through the liquid and make the explosive vapour. Daimler proved the mobility of this engine by fitting it to a bicycle, held upright by two small outrigger wheels, and superintending a successful 3km test run by his son Paul on 10 November 1885. Next year he installed an engine at the rear of a shaftless carriage and achieved 10mph with a 1½hp engine. In 1889 he rationalised the four-stroke system by building a two-cylinder V-type engine using the one crankshaft, with the cycles so timed that uniformly distributed impulses were given to the shaft.

When manufacturers of both motor cars and aeroplanes had settled on petrol-driven internal combustion engines, the way was at least clear for oddballs to make this freak transfer of a 23-litre Maybach aero-engine into a racing motor car—Count Zborowski's famous Chitty Chitty Bang Bang of 1921.

It was this engine that positively attracted the attention of forward-looking engineers, with its capability as a power unit for automobiles. But even before the two-cycle development the Daimler engine had been put into the air. Dr Karl Wölfert installed one of Daimler's earliest internal combustion engines in an airship he launched in 1888. Owing to faulty body construction, the airship was wrecked almost immediately, before the engine could be satisfactorily tested. Wölfert persisted, but in a later test near Berlin the airship exploded, and Wölfert and his mechanic, Knabe, were burnt to death in the ensuing blaze.

Benz, working independently, had been keeping step with Daimler, and actually produced his practical mobile internal combustion engine first, in the spring of 1885. He mounted a single-cylinder four-stroke water-cooled engine at the rear of a specially built three-wheeler light car. The engine produced ⅔hp at 250rpm. Benz at this time was using a surface carburettor with saturated wicks protruding from it, across which hot air was blown—the carburettor that sprays fuel in a fine jet into a stream of air moving through the choke was to come later. But Benz's ignition system was individual and modern: his own invention of the battery, coil and sparking plug, which is used almost unchanged today. Like Daimler, Benz started by using benzene as his fuel (the name has no connection with his), but in a historic change he took up the volatile liquid obtained from that refinement of petroleum (rock oil) which contains as its main constituent the fraction (the component separately released during progressive fractional distillation) called gasoline. This is a cumbersome but accurate way to introduce into the history of flight the explosive spirit called *petrol*, but petrol is the original given name of motor spirit and aviation spirit for internal combustion engines; strictly considered, *gasoline*, adopted in America and afterwards elsewhere, confuses the part with the whole.

Daimler, too, turned to petrol. Although he started the Daimler Motor Company in Germany in 1890 as a full-fledged automobile-manufacturing enterprise, it was the export of his engines, and the manufacture of his engines by other car-constructors under licence, which exercised him most. Emile Levassor, of the French firm of Panhard and Levassor, then making band-saws at Ivry, snapped up the French licence for Daimlers. He sublet the concession to Peugeot (Les Fils de Peugeot Frères) of Doubs, which produced their own cars, not always with Daimler engines; indeed they were soon developing their own. F. W. Lanchester, as famous in aeronautics as in automobilism, eventually took up the Daimler licence in England. An Austrian named Emil Jellinek working in France had a franchise for Daimler engines, but quickly confounded historians by deriving a new engine from their principle, which he called Mercédès, after his daughter.

Emile Roger had already bought the rights to the Benz engines, which subsequently were sublet in France to Hurtu. Delahaye built their first cars around the Benz. Roger swiftly put the Benz engine in a four-wheeler. Levassor transferred the Daimler engine to the front

Power runs amok in the Race of Death. The Paris–Madrid automobile road race of 1903, in which so many drivers, mechanics and spectators had been killed by the time the leaders reached Bordeaux that the French Government stopped the race, and the cortège never reached Madrid. This holocaust, only 10 years after the advent of practical motoring in Europe and seven months before the Wrights first flew in America, was the culmination of the astonishing development of the internal combustion engine in pursuit of power. Fernand Gabriel, starting No 168 in a 70hp Mors, passed over eighty of his rivals, alive or dead, on the road and finished at Bordeaux, having driven the 342 miles at an average of over 65mph. Loraine Barrow, driving a De Dietrich, had swerved to avoid a dog and crashed into a tree, killing his mechanic. Another Englishman was burnt to death under his car. Leslie Porter, in a Wolseley, hit a house when he could not stop for a level crossing and killed his mechanic. Tourand, in a Brouhot, swerved to avoid a child but still killed the child and several other spectators. Marcel Renault, in the light car in which he had won the Paris–Vienna, overtook a rival baby Decauville south of Poitiers and crashed, killing his mechanic and fatally injuring himself. Louis Renault, who was clocked at just under 90mph on a stretch near Chartres, passed Charles Jarrott's much more powerful 45hp De Dietrich on the final stretch, finished second at 62.3mph, and immediately sped back to the deathbed of his brother.

The successful one-off 12hp Wright aero-engine of 1903, designed from scratch by Orville and Wilbur Wright and installed in the Wright Flyer I to make the machine the first aeroplane to achieve controlled powered flight: a front view of its original installation.

of the Panhard–Levassor, though Peugeot temporarily retained it at the rear. The Comte De Dion, who had previously been making steam-powered automobiles, switched to the petrol principle, built a successful single-cylinder air-cooled engine, and followed it with a striking succession of 8, 10 and 15hp machines. Levassor built a new engine of his own design, deriving from Daimler, and called it the Phénix, with two in-line cylinders of 80mm bore and 120mm stroke, giving a capacity of 1,206cc and a rating of 4hp, still at 750rpm. Then he added two more cylinders, giving a capacity of 2,413cc and a rating of 8hp. Peugeot designed their own two-cylinder engine with an 84 × 126mm bore and stroke giving 1,395cc, then enlarged it to 2,186cc and—only four years after they had started manufacturing—expanded this to 3,324cc (10hp rating) with 115 × 160mm cylinders. Within another four years a Panhard car (Levassor died at the turn of the century) rated 70hp with four cylinders of 160 × 170mm and a capacity of 13·7 litres.

No such extravagance in the inefficient use of sheer power was to be encountered until just after World War I, when Count Louis Zborowski put a 23 litre Maybach aeroplane engine from a German Gotha bomber into an old chain-drive Mercédès chassis and raced it at Brooklands as Chitty-Chitty-Bang-Bang. Then he put an 18·8 litre Benz aeroplane engine into another Mercédès as Chitty II, and built two more aero-engined Chittys before he was killed at Monza in 1924. But this was all happening 20 years earlier.

The Panhard 13·7 litre was built for the Paris–Vienna race of 1902,

Steam engines were used in automobiles during the first 30 years of motor transport. By 1910 the 10hp Stanley Steamer was a popular light runabout and a public-relations missionary for automobilism.

which was in fact won by Marcel Renault driving one of his own light cars, although one of the giants, with a rating of 60hp, had kept up 70mph over the first 50 miles. Renault maintained 39mph for 15 hours 46 minutes. The climax came next year when the notorious Race of Death, the Paris–Madrid marathon, was cancelled at the halfway stage because of the carnage.

At that time not one single man-carrying powered aeroplane had properly flown. Later in the year Wilbur Wright flew for half a mile in 59 seconds (ie, at 30½mph) in the Wright Flyer I powered by a 12hp petrol-fuelled internal combustion engine designed and built by Wilbur and Orville Wright.

The date of this historic event was 17 December 1903. The altogether individual approach of the Wrights to the art of flying, when compared with their rivals in the far more ancient European tradition, will be examined shortly. The significant decision of immediate moment was their determination to build as their own power unit an internal combustion engine. They would have used an established automobile engine if one had been suitable. They recorded:

We wrote to a number of the best known automobile manufacturers in an endeavor to secure a motor for the new machine. Not receiving favorable answers from any of these, we proceeded to design a motor of our own, from which we hoped to secure about eight horse-power. When the motor was tested it gave more power than we had anticipated. It developed a little over 12 horsepower [*sic*] and weighed about 160 pounds, without magneto, water, or oil.

Emitting for the moment only a small whistle of wonder that these men could construct swiftly and without heroics an engine more efficient than any tested motor then available to them—and a slightly shriller blast that they then turned nonchalantly to designing, from basic mechanical principles, propellers of then unparalleled efficiency—we may note that the Wrights had quietly signed the death warrant of the steam engine for air transport. At that time the decision was not such a foregone conclusion as it may appear now.

Steam-driven automobiles had been introduced before those driven by internal combustion engines, and for over a decade they were serious rivals to the lighter machine. In the first automobile race in history, the 79-mile Paris–Rouen Trial of 22 July 1894, a De Dion steamer came in first at an average speed of 11·6mph, ahead of nine Panhard–Levassors and Peugeots with Daimler engines, although the steamer was disqualified for technical reasons. A De Dion steamer won first prize in the Marseille–Nice–La Turbie race of 1897, covering 145 miles, which included the gruelling Corniche roads, at over 18mph. A 15hp De Dion–Bouton steam carriage achieved 38mph for the first 144 miles of the Paris–Bordeaux–Paris race of 1895 before breaking down at Vouvray. In the (literally) murderous Paris–Bordeaux section of the cancelled Paris–Madrid race run several months before the Wrights flew in 1903, a Serpollet steamer at least finished the 342-mile stage, though only at 17mph. In the United States the Stanley steamers, marketed for a time as Locomobiles and burning 'gasoline', were the light runabouts that initially popularised motoring in the country, and Stanley Steamers were manufactured until 1925. Léon Serpollet's steamer, the Easter Egg, had put up the world speed record to 75mph a year before the Wrights flew, and over the next four years, at Ormond Beach, Florida, the specially designed racer called the Stanley Rocket, driven by Fred Marriot, pushed up the record five times to an incredible 127·6mph in 1906; in a further attack during the following year the Rocket's speedometer was showing 197mph when the machine broke up, literally in the air—as was Fred Marriot himself at that moment.

Steam power, therefore, was not an obvious non-starter for consideration as the propellant for air transport. Steam had been used for model ornithopters and helicopters since 1830. Over the 20 years between 1848 and 1868 John Stringfellow and Félix du Temple alternated productions of steam-driven models, and although du Temple's practical full-size aeroplane is believed to have taken off under the power of a gas engine for its triumphant début of 1874, it could well, then or later, have been powered by the steam engine that seems to be fitted to it in one illustration of the event. Certainly the brothers Félix and Louis du Temple later installed a steam engine in the same machine, and in 1876 they patented a light steam boiler which, with a then attractive weight–power ratio of around 40lb per hp, was the prototype for many subsequent engines.

One year after the du Temple take-off at Brest the English engineer Thomas Moy built a steam engine weighing 80lb and developing 3hp, which he installed in a tandem-wing monoplane of about 15ft wing-span. Either in deference to Henson, or in an attempt to borrow his withered laurels, he called his creation the Aerial Steamer, and ran it tethered to a central fountain on a circular track at the Crystal Palace, in south London. Propelled by twin fan-type airscrews 6ft in diameter, the steamer did lift some 6in off the ground, but there was no semblance of aerial control and, of course, no pilot. The whole contraption weighed some 120lb.

In a further tribute to Henson, Captain Alexander Mozhaiski of the Russian Navy built an endearing full-size monoplane based in extraordinary detail on the design of the original Ariel and powered by a steam engine specially built in London 'for aeronautical purposes'. He tested it at Krasnoye Selo, near St Petersburg, in 1884. It was a man-carrying machine in the sense that it had a pilot, I. N. Golubev, aboard, but there is no evidence that Golubev had a clue about flying it, and he certainly was given no chance to do so. The steamer was launched down a ski-jump ramp and it was claimed that it had remained airborne for 20 or 30m after the fall away of the run-down. The aircraft then hit the ground and never rose again, duplicating the powered take-off and the subsequent dejected return to the drawing board registered by du Temple 10 years earlier.

Contemporarily with Mozhaiski the very accomplished French electrical engineer Clément Ader, who had acquired an early fortune from developing telephone equipment but had a private passion for aeronautics, began to construct a powered aeroplane. He chose steam as his medium, and designed a very efficient light engine. He installed this in a striking bat-winged monoplane, which he named Éole, and personally piloted it in a historic test at Armainvilliers in 1890. Witnesses said that it took off from level ground and was airborne for some 50m, but not even Ader then claimed that this very creditable powered take-off was a sustained flight. Sixteen years later he alleged that he had made a further flight of 100m in Éole in 1891, but this claim has been authoritatively refuted. Commissioned by the French War Ministry, Ader went on to construct a series of further machines, which crystallised into a complicated movable-wing twin-engined steamer called Avion III. During two tests of this machine on a circular track in October 1897 Ader completed one circuit under power, but always earthbound, and then succumbed to a gust of wind, which blew him off the track and put him *hors de combat*. Nine years later he claimed, again falsely, that he had achieved a smooth flight of 300m in Avion III.

The climax of the heavyweight contest to launch a steam-powered aeroplane was signalled by the huffing and puffing generated by Hiram Stevens Maxim. Maxim, born an American citizen in Maine but later becoming a naturalised Briton, was an extremely capable operator, who diminished his own reputation by writing too many flourishes into his own fanfares. Trained as a naval architect and later as an electrical engineer, Maxim became a very thrusting business-man after his invention of the Maxim quick-firing gun (producing 10 shots a second) and his entry into the Vickers armaments consortium. By 1887 he was convinced that aeronautics was not only a feasible but a profitable concept for the future, and in 1889 the Vickers directors gave him financial support in a long-term project to construct a large aircraft designed to convey passengers.

At this crucial moment Maxim opted for steam power, although he had originally intended to develop Otto-type gas engines. He did not grasp the potential of the internal combustion engine in spite of the fact that Daimler's two-cylinder V-type engine was then on show at the Paris Exhibition. It is true that the first Panhard–Levassor motor car incorporating this engine was not sold until 1891, but Levassor had had the skill to project its successful future, and it may be held against Maxim that he did not. On the other hand Maxim, to his great credit as a visionary, was aiming uncompromisingly for big size. He wanted to construct a machine that would transport a payload weighing several thousand pounds. In the 1890s, the decade of his most concentrated experimentation, reliance

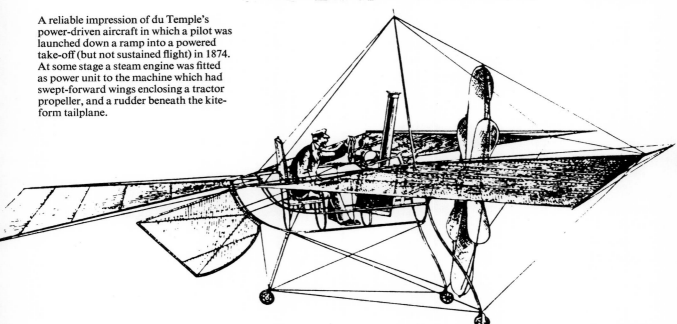

A reliable impression of du Temple's power-driven aircraft in which a pilot was launched down a ramp into a powered take-off (but not sustained flight) in 1874. At some stage a steam engine was fitted as power unit to the machine which had swept-forward wings enclosing a tractor propeller, and a rudder beneath the kite-form tailplane.

on steam may have seemed the more correct solution—even after Maxim's most successful effort the Comte de Dion was racing steam carriages and Léon Bollée putting an eight-seater steam omnibus on the grid for speed and endurance contests in France.

While he was developing a suitable aero engine, Maxim began to superintend further research in an admirably wide field. He built a wind tunnel, tested and recorded the aerodynamic reaction of a series of wing sections, and emerged with a selection of cambered wings labelled with the details of lift and resistance apposite to their individual shapes. He tested various arrangements of these sections, and concluded a theoretical ideal of a multiplane format, equipping a sharply dihedral biplane with three auxiliary wings, to be rigged almost at will, as when a barque crowded on more sail. He built a whirling arm with an eventual girder radius of 50m (including an attached wire) so that he could test models in the air at 80mph around a 1,000ft orbit. He experimented with propeller construction and shape, torsion and strength, until he produced the design of laminated wood that was later adopted as standard for three decades. Again in advance of the practice of the time, he designed his aircraft of tubular steel construction with oxyacetylene-welded side trusses—all this before an aeroplane had ever flown.

Maxim proposed to run the 8,000lb 104ft wing-span aircraft he was creating from two independent pusher propellers nearly 18ft long, driven by two engines each developing 181hp but weighing only 1,800lb, together with the specially designed boiler (weighing 2,400lb, including water and the naphtha, which was burnt from 7,560 jets in a continuous 'square bed' of flame 20in deep). This concentration of weight was correctly sited so that the centre of gravity of the machine was accurately related to the position of the wings.

Moy's Aerial Steamer, a 15ft wing-span model weighing 120lb with a 3hp steam engine, ran like a dog on a leash round a circular track in 1875. It did lift off, but never flew.

Much more lovingly based on Henson's Aerial Steamer was Alexander Mozhaiski's steam-powered monoplane. It took off by plunging down a ski-jump ramp in 1884— and sailed on for far less distance than a modern ski-jumper. An English steam engine drove a large tractor propeller backed by two smaller pusher propellers cut into the trailing-edges of the main-plane. Its untrained pilot could take little action, except to pray.

After seven years' work Hiram S. Maxim was ready for take-off. His creation was not yet a 'flying machine', although it was always called so. Its covered wings were of a finely calculated camber, but it did not yet have its full wing-span, and it did not have directional steering (except by individual variation of the speeds of the airscrews). It did, however, possess elevators. Maxim was at the time concerned only to test the lifting capacity of his design—recorded, even before take-off, by measuring the tension of springs between airframe and undercarriage—and for this purpose the kite-formation of the lifting surfaces of the centre section of the aeroplane was deemed sufficient; tapered dihedral extensions of the mainplane were not fitted.

Maxim knew that it would take much time and experience to learn to control the machine in the air, and therefore he contrived that it could not lift more than 2ft off the ground. He achieved this by running the machine on heavy iron wheels along a straight railway track, 1,800ft long, of wide 9ft gauge, and having two other raised wooden rails mounted on posts 2ft above the ground, each guard rail 13ft on the outside of the steel rails. Under the guard rail ran disengaged wheels mounted on outriggers from the machine's fuselage. If the craft rose 2ft in the air, the extra wheels engaged, and ran along the underside of the wooden 'horizontal fence', thus keeping

A very advanced light steam engine developing some 20hp drove Clément Ader's eerie bat-winged Éole, which took off from level ground in 1890 with Ader fussing over complicated controls that were intended to reproduce many of the movements of the bat's wing except actual flapping. Airborne for only 50m, and as blind as a bat because he had placed the pilot's seat behind a tall boiler, Ader had no time to test these mechanical aids.

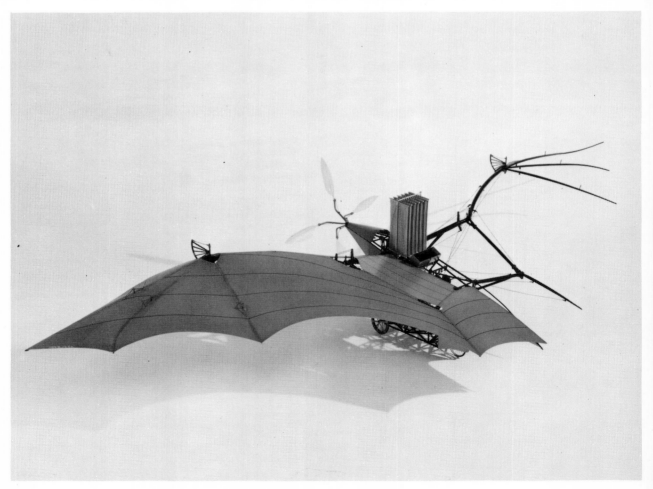

the machine from rising higher. The locomotive had no brakes and was restrained at the end of its 1,800ft run by three ropes stretched across the end of the track and working on tension capstans.

On 31 July 1894 Maxim boarded his machine with his additional crew of three—one to work the elevators and two to shout out the dial readings, while Maxim himself twirled the wheels of the throttles. They prepared for flight. While steam pressure was being increased and the propellers screwed into the air, the craft was tethered to a dynamometer. Maxim ran up the steam pressure to 2,200lb per sq in. As the machine strained, throbbing at its mooring, Maxim suddenly gave the signal for release, and the two dial-watchers were thrown to the slatted floor with the acceleration. Recovering his own balance while his chief continued to open the throttles, Tom Jackson, the Number One, shifted the elevator controls and the craft edged upwards. Maxim recounted:

> We soon obtained a speed of 42 m.p.h., when all [guard] wheels were seen to be running on the upper track, and revolving in the opposite direction from those on the lower track. After running about 1000 feet, one of the restraining axletrees [of the guard wheels] doubled up. This put the lift of the machine on to the other three. The upper track was broken, the machine was liberated and floated in the air, giving those on board the sensation of being in a boat. However, a piece of the broken

Ader brought in two 20hp steam engines to drive his Avion III, again of simulated bat-wing construction, with variable sweep-back wings intended to shift the centre of pressure during flight. Ader falsely claimed that he flew for 300m in this machine in 1897. Avion III was constructed as the result of a commission from the French War Ministry, the first indication by any government of a practical interest, backed by central finance, in the development of the flying machine. This picture is faked.

"FIGARO ILLUSTRE"

track caught in one of the screws: at the same instant I shut off the steam, and the machine stopped and settled to the ground. . . . It was the first time in the world that a powered flying machine had actually lifted itself, and its crew, into the air.

One wing was wrecked, the others were displaced, and the fuselage was distorted. There was proof enough that the quartet had 'flown', or at least been lifted by 'making a surface support a given weight by the application of power to the resistance of air'. The freshly painted rims of the guard wheels had made a continuous mark on the underside of the guard rails.

Possibly Maxim boasted too much of his incomplete achievement, for most historians say he never did another thing with his partially wrecked machine, but merely talked about his 'triumph'. He certainly never went on to practise steering and control in freer flight. But he did rebuild, he did make further designs, within three years even patenting a four-rotor helicopter. The flying machine was restored to full operational efficiency, as far as it had progressed, an action which has escaped most aeronautical writers, but they have omitted to research the royal archives; for in the summer after the crash of 1894 Maxim invited to his test ground at Baldwyns Park, Bexley, the then Duke of York, afterwards King George V. The Duke went aboard the machine. Again the pressure against the mooring was increased until there was a screw thrust of 2,000lb. Maxim had the machine cut loose and it plunged forward. 'For God's sake, slow up!' roared the Duke's escort, Admiral of the Fleet Sir George Commerell. 'No! Let her go for all she's worth!' countermanded Prince George. The future King George V, a very careful and reserved man who was not inclined to exaggerate the wonders of nature or man, recorded in his diary that night: 'It made two runs for me to see. I was in it for one of them; it did lift off the ground part of the time.'

Many years later, when the Duke of York became king, he gave Maxim a knighthood. Undoubtedly Sir Hiram Maxim did too little in the aeronautical field for all the expense he incurred, and talked too much. He unctuously wrote in 1908 after a nil achievement over the preceding decade: 'It is very gratifying to me to know that all the successful flying machines of today are built on the lines which I had thought out [in 1893 and 1894]. . . . I had reasoned out the best type of a machine even before I commenced a stroke of the work.'

Part of the truth about Maxim is, without doubt, that he had plenty to do and plenty to earn, not only in the armament world but in other spheres of achievement, by no means always in Great Britain. Some of this private enterprise may present the clue to his virtual abandonment of the flying machine as powered by steam. In 1896 he was concerned in harnessing factories in the United States to manufacture the automobiles designed by his son, Hiram Percy Maxim, which were marketed as Columbias. The system of propulsion chosen was the petrol ('gasoline') engine. In reality this was no revolutionary change. In his youth he had studied and developed both steam and internal combustion engines, and had invented an automatic gas

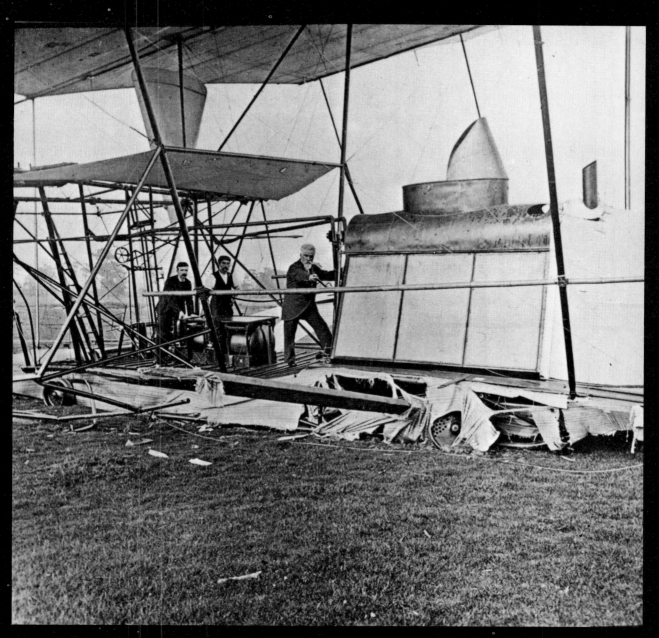

Maxim stands impotently at the throttles
after his machine had soared higher than
intended (that is, over 2ft altitude) and the
restraining frame broke up and fouled an
airscrew, 31 July 1894.

engine. The helicopter that Maxim *père* was planning in 1897 had an internal combustion engine, driven by exploding acetylene. But when Hiram Percy Maxim came down for petrol he came down in a very big way, having also risked going up a much longer distance while making up his mind. He cheerfully described his introduction to the explosive mixture:

My first experiment was a rough 'get acquainted' test. My idea of such a test was to introduce a drop [of gasoline] out of the bottle into an empty six-pounder cartridge case and then touch it off. I began with one drop [plugging the 12-inch case and rolling it around a few times]. I was excited, for I felt this might be a historic moment for me. Standing back, I scratched the match and tossed it in. There was a short and very ominous pause. Then the end of the world came, it seemed to me. There was a terrifying explosion, fire shot up out of the cartridge case, the latter

Hiram S. Maxim's 8,000lb 'flying machine' (strictly, a lift test-rig) powered by two 181hp steam engines and manned by a crew of four. In 1894 it took off, without directional steering, and was airborne for some 600ft.

staggered drunkenly on the bench, and the match I had thrown in went hurtling to the ceiling. It was evident that there was about a thousand times more kick in a drop of gasoline than I had pictured in my wildest flights of imagination.

If that experience seems to depict a somewhat naive approach from a man who was the nephew of an inventor of high explosives, the son of the inventor of automatic weaponry, and himself the inventor of a silencer for firearms, it may merely demonstrate that all the Maxims had a slightly unscientific gift of the gab. But, for what it was worth, it was the outward and visible sign that Hiram Stevens Maxim was lining up with the Wright brothers—or possibly in his own estimation ahead of them—in the resolution of the conflict of thought concerning the struggle over power in aeronautical machines.

The extreme stage of early development of the aeroplane of maximum equilibrium: the first 'undisputed truly stable general-purpose aeroplane', the prototype BE2c of 1913 compared with Geoffrey de Havilland's original BE2 of 1912, from which it was developed by Britain's Royal Aircraft Factory at Farnborough after specialist research by Edward T. Busk of the National Physical Laboratory. Improved stability came from the staggering of the wings, which were vertically symmetrical in the modifications as far as the BE2b, from a revised tailplane and a directional fin. The wing-span was 37ft and area 371sq ft. It could climb up to 10,000ft in 45 minutes, had a maximum speed of 72mph at 6,500ft, and could stay up for 3¼ hours—no mean performance only 4 years after Blériot had flown across the Channel to about 100yd past the white cliffs of Dover at 137ft in 37 minutes. Some 3,500 BE2cs were mass-produced in the 1914–1918 war. They cost about £800 each, plus £500 for the RAF (Royal Aircraft *Factory*) V-type eight-cylinder 90hp engine. It was a fault in the fuel pipe of the prototype of this engine that killed Ted Busk. In one sense the BE2c was destroyed by its own stability. It was used mainly in wartime as a reconnaissance scout, using the excellent visibility afforded by the staggered lower wing, though the observer's initial armament was a revolver. Later, though fitted with a sideways firing Lewis .303in machine gun, and with a capacity of 224lb of bombs fixed below the wing, it became notorious as 'Fokker-fodder', its rock-like stability depriving it of the manoeuvrability necessary to engage the faster and handier Fokker *EIII* single-seater monoplane with a 7.92mm Spandau machine gun forward-firing through the propeller arc by means of interrupter-gear.

The word *slogan*, originally Gaelic, began its life in Scotland in the fifteenth century with the meaning of a battle-cry—'To heaven the Border slogan rung'. It finished on Madison Avenue in the twentieth century with the meaning of a magic term that absolves the user from thinking about what he is saying—a ju-ju that James Bryant Conant of Harvard called 'a powerful opiate for the conscience'. This mutation is also accurate as an account of the progressive use of the word *stability* in nineteenth-century aerodynamics. It began as a sine qua non and it ended as a shibboleth. The whole significance of stability had to be rethought during a vital few years before its essential validity as an aerodynamic necessity could be freshly accepted.

From 1804 until 1909 designers were trying to build aeroplanes that would maintain their attitude in the air virtually automatically, with minimum correction, by means of 'inherent stability', which the constructors hoped they had built into the machine. The flight of an aeroplane as projected by the designers came very close to being an idealisation of the flight of the schoolboy's paper dart: like a dog

Forty-two years before Busk's BE2c, Alphonse Pénaud had produced, in 1871, this Planophore, the first inherently stable aeroplane to influence aircraft design. It was a rubber-driven (pusher-propeller) practical model, 20in long with a wing-span of 18in and area of 76sq in. The upwards curve of the tips of the mainplane and tailplane provided lateral stability, and longitudinal stability came from setting the tailplane at a negative angle of 8 degrees to the chord-line of the main wings.

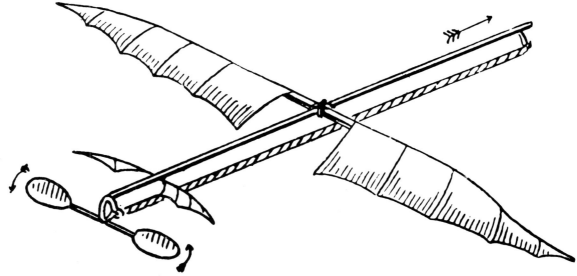

walking on its hind legs, the wonder was not that it was done well but that it was done at all. This was understandable enough while models alone were being used, and occasionally flown with success; for only an inherent stability would allow them to continue in the air. But there was less obvious justification for total reliance on built-in stability once pilots were put aboard to take over control of an aircraft should it ever freely rise into the air.

In 105 years this very rarely happened. By 31 December 1908 only nine men in addition to the Wright brothers had maintained themselves in the air in a powered aeroplane for more than a minute. Of these, six had stayed aloft, by a charitable estimate, for around the

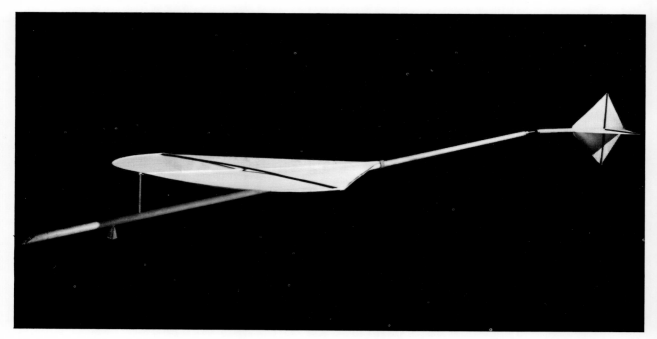

Sir George Cayley's model glider of 1804, seen here in accurate reconstruction, offered roughly twice the wing area, and had its cruciform tail unit set at a positive angle of 11½ degrees to the rod forming the main horizontal beam, and the kite-form mainplane set at 6 degrees to this beam. Cayley wrote, with some exaggeration, that with this configuration 'it would proceed uniformly in a right line for ever'. Pénaud's Planophore, which did not 'proceed for ever' but did fly 131ft in 11 seconds before the gravest technical witnesses, enshrined in the minds of the French, who were the most serious aircraft designers in Europe, the ideal of predominant equilibrium, or inherent stability, which culminated in the BE2c of Great Britain.

bare 60 seconds. The other three were Henry Farman, with a record of 44 minutes, Léon Delagrange with 30 minutes, and Louis Blériot with a maximum of 11 minutes, achieved just nine months before he made history with the first flight across the English Channel. Wilbur Wright himself had notched a flight of 2 hours, 20 minutes, 23 seconds, covering 78 miles.

The Wrights were flying *inherently unstable* aircraft. This was their choice, their deliberate design, because they rated as the most desirable factor in the fusion of man and machine the mastery of the pilot in continuous control during every second of the duration of flight. Farman, Delagrange and Blériot were *minding* machines intended to be stable but subject to intermittent correction by the pilot. After 1908, when they had witnessed in France Wilbur Wright's beautifully executed control of his own machine in accurate and (aerodynamically) comparatively effortless banking and circling, they adapted some of the flight-control principles of the Wrights, which enabled them to achieve smoother manoeuvrability. From this time, as it was later realised, the Wrights had shot their bolt as significant and indeed unique aerial pioneers. Increasingly the Europeans became *aeronauts*, adapting the machine and training the man to achieve a more complete fusion of the two finite members in this potentially infinite symbiosis.

The Wrights, on their side, modified their aeroplanes to take in that 'European' essential of inherent stability, the fixed tailplane, which Sir George Cayley had advocated in 1804; and later they accepted rear elevators. There was experimentation on both sides in lateral control (ie, avoiding having the aeroplane rolling as if its fuselage were a barrel) between the Wright's system of wing-warping and the European use of ailerons—theoretically a better proposition, but quite useless until the Europeans copied from the Wrights (who

Goupil's monoplane of 1884 was designed to duplicate the body of a bird as well as its wings. The novel feature was the inclusion—separately placed and not set in the wings—of elevons, the projecting control surfaces intended to act not only as elevators but as opposite-acting ailerons for control of roll. But they were not linked to the rudder action. Goupil's steam engine intended as the power plant for this graceful machine was built but never installed in the airframe. But in 1917 Glenn Curtiss, who was trying to break the Wright patents on wing-warping—which the Wrights had said as early as 1908 included wing-tip ailerons—reconstructed the Goupil machine with a petrol engine and flew it. Between-wings ailerons in a biplane (most nearly corresponding to Goupil's design for the monoplane) had been adopted by Curtiss much earlier, as in the seaplane pictured here.

had learned through practical flying) to link rudder movement with the variation of angle on the wing surfaces. Then the two schools merged—the pragmatic constructors who had adapted their craft to the elements they encountered while developing intuitive flying, and the courageous coachmen who had intellectualised an ethereal machine that they intended to keep in the air by guess or by god. From the year 1913, when the British BE2c rose into the sky above Laffan's Plain at Farnborough as the first undisputed truly stable general-purpose aeroplane, there were no separate sects in basic aerodynamics.

The designer of the BE2c was of a characteristic new breed. Ted Busk was a 27-year-old mountaineer and engineer, a university contemporary of Rupert Brooke, who had begun his technical studies at Cambridge already familiar with the concept that flying machines were details of reality, no longer of fantasy. He joined the National Physical Laboratory at Farnborough and was immediately set to specialising on aeroplane stability. He was a test-pilot scientist who checked all his wind-tunnel work by literally flying his experimental aircraft with no hands. In November 1914 he was burnt to death over Laffan's Plain in his BE2c, not through any fault of stability but from a fuel leak in a prototype new engine he was testing. In the next year the last edition of a Wright aeroplane was constructed by Orville—Wilbur had died in 1912. It was a workmanlike but not particularly distinguished single-seat military biplane, and it had ailerons on both sets of wings.

The early aeroplane-builders in Europe had very clear ideas of the stability they were trying to achieve—preferably built in to the aircraft with no necessity for constant correction—and they knew what additional control they required to vary the attitude or course of the aircraft wilfully and purposefully. Stability was essential in two dimensions, the vertical and the horizontal planes, but control was desirable in two aspects of each dimension. This is best explained, not entirely accurately, by considering the centrifugal force exerted on someone who is riding a bicycle.

A cyclist riding at a fair speed who wishes to turn on a prolonged left-hand circle has to do more than merely shift his handlebars. Altering the direction of the front wheel will theoretically project the bicycle on a left-hand turn, but the theory only works at the point where the wheel is in friction with the road, and then not very well. The centrifugal force exerted by the weight of the bicycle and its rider swings the machine outwards. At slow speeds there is a side-slip that is only transferred into manageable motion by the friction of the tyres on the road. At fast speeds not even the tyres hold, and there is a crash caused by the unrestrained impetus of the upper part of the machine and the rider. The cyclist learns to counter this tendency by taking additional action besides turning his handlebars. He leans into the centre of the bend—if he were a pilot he would call it rolling—and forces the weight of machine and rider more directly on to the tyres.

In this way he has exerted control in two aspects of the horizontal plane: he has controlled direction by simple steering, and he has resisted drift due to centrifugal force. In the vertical plane also there are two aspects of control to be considered, but because he is on a bicycle and not flying in the air, he does little about them except follow the track and physically adjust to the effects. If he is riding along a switchback road at considerable speed, he has merely to keep his handlebars straight with a relaxed rigidity, and the actual course in the vertical plane is followed by the interaction of his own weight and the contours of the road. Centrifugal force is exerted, but is mastered with comparative ease. Going fast down and up, into and out of a hollow, the downward centrifugal force is absorbed by the pneumatic tyres and the sprung construction of the wheels; the rider does go marginally downwards in an extra curve, but this movement is contained by a minor distortion in the shape of the machine. Going fast up and down, over the crest of a hump, the upward centrifugal force expresses itself in a leap off the ground that is soon countered by gravity. In practice, therefore, the cyclist, by skilfully balancing a well designed machine, achieves stability in two dimensions and exercises control in three aspects. In the horizontal plane he is concerned with two aspects—changing direction and opposing side-slip. In the vertical plane he changes altitude, but really does precious little even about that.

For not exactly similar reasons, since the mechanics of flight are more complicated than the mechanics of cycling or even sailing, the would-be designer of an aeroplane sought stability in two dimensions and control in three aspects. He needed *longitudinal stability* in the plane of symmetry, ie, in the vertical plane which contains the nose and tail of an aeroplane and the backbone of a centrally seated pilot. He required his aircraft to be able to neutralise unsolicited motion that would incline his pilot's spine forwards or backwards, as when, in the ocean of the air, a craft pitches or tosses (plunges nose-down or heaves nose-up). He also required *longitudinal control*, or control in pitch, so that the pilot could initiate or cancel motion that took him bodily with his craft upwards or downwards.

In the horizontal plane he needed lateral stability in order to cope with any movement out of the plane of symmetry, ie, any movement of the pilot's spine that was either sideways or rotating. (Rotating would initially move the spine sideways and downwards.) He could divide these necessary corrective qualities into two. Just as longitudinal stability was the requirement to maintain a desired height, 'sideways' stability was the requirement for an aircraft to maintain a course, suppressing or correcting the swings off-course that are called yaws. This is *directional stability*. But in order to change course accurately he needed reliable steering with resistance to the tendency to go off at a tangent in a turn because of side-slip, and resistance to other tendencies induced by one or other of his control surfaces; as when a fixed vertical fin, subject to air pressure from one side, tends to rotate the aircraft horizontally in a circle of which the fin is the circumference. Ability to correct these and other tendencies constitutes *directional control*. Any unsought rotation of the aeroplane about its longitudinal axis would ideally be countered by the constructor having built into his machine *stability in roll*. When later, like sophisticated cyclists, pilots found that they could use roll to affect the behaviour of their aircraft, they demanded control in roll, which is most often referred to by what is literally the more embracing term, *lateral control*.

These were the six requirements of the aircraft designer. (They were the wish-fulfilment of airship constructors even more poignantly than of aeroplane-builders.)

Longitudinal stability.
Longitudinal control.
Directional stability.
Directional control.
Stability in roll.
Lateral control.

Theory was a little smoother in the early days, because, although everybody yearned for a suitably light prime mover, the fact that no practical engine existed relieved designers of the problems raised by the torque of an airscrew—or even of the little matter of the turbulence that would have been set up by the proposed banks of paddles, to be set like oars in the quinqueremes of Nineveh. There was one true aeroplane form of incalculable antiquity that was available as a model. The kite had been in existence for at least 3,000 years. The kite is an aeroplane, not mechanically driven, which derives lift from the thrust of air applied at a correct angle against its planes.

Sir George Cayley had used a kite as the mainplane for the first successful and reconstructible (ie, not evolved by an unrepeatable accident) aeroplane in history. This was his 5ft-long glider of 1804, which had three positive factors of stability. The long pole consti-

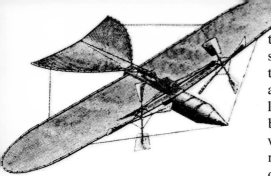

Thirty-eight years of endeavour span
Victor Tatin's major productions of
aircraft design. His practical 6ft wing-span
twin-screw model monoplane of 1879 was
powered by compressed air contained in
the barrel forming the fuselage. Having
flown for 15m, it probably represents
Tatin's most undisputed achievement in
his long aeronautical career.

tuting the fuselage had the kite mainplane inclined backwards at the
slight angle of six degrees to the baseline of trailing-edge to nose;
there was a cruciform tail unit attached by a universal joint, adjustable but in the successful test set at $11\frac{1}{2}$ degrees droop from the baseline of nose to tail; and a variable centre of gravity was made possible
by mounting a weight on a skewer point and sticking it into the
wooden body-pole at selected positions. (It is well forward, like a
nose-wheel, in Cayley's own sketch of this 1804 glider, which is the
one he previously referred to when he mentioned that 'it was very
pretty to see it sail down a steep hill'. See page 40.)

Dealing here only with the stability of the aeroplane, the kite form
of mainplane was sounder for equilibrium than for lift, though the
trim of the glider as Cayley had adjusted the gravity weight presented
the wing at a satisfactory 20 degrees from the horizontal, and maintained a favourably low gravity position. The fixed surfaces of the

The Tatin-de-la-Vaulx monoplane
powered by a 50hp Antoinette engine
driving two pusher propellers made two
hops at Saint-Cyr in November 1907, but
crash-landed after the second lift and was
never reconstructed. Tatin's stream-lined
Aéro-Torpille, with a pusher propeller at
extreme aft as in a naval torpedo, was an
eye-opener at exhibitions but a failure in
the field.

cruciform tail unit, with both vertical and horizontal planes acting as
a combined rudder and elevator control, provide adequate longitudinal and lateral stability.

Cayley was very well aware that he was seeking positive stability
and control—what he called 'these principles upon which the support,
steadiness, elevation, depression and steerage of vessels for aerial
navigation depend'. In 1808 he built a full-size glider, presumed but
not confirmed to have been man-carrying, of which he reported: 'Its
steerage and steadiness were perfectly proved, and it would sail
obliquely downward in any direction according to the set of the
rudder.'

In 1809 Cayley wrote and published a long paper called 'On Aerial
Navigation' in which he dealt at some length with stability. He first
expounded *lateral dihedral*—the construction of wings not in a continuous plane, as in the kite mainplane of his first glider, but having
them sprout from the fuselage in a shallow V. 'This angular form,
with the apex downward, is the chief basis of stability in aerial navi-

gation', he said. He then dealt with longitudinal stability, pointing out that when an aircraft was pitching, the downward plunge of the nose shifted the centre of pressure backwards and the upward heave pulled it forwards, and with the centre of gravity correctly placed by the designer this pendulum movement was a reinforcement to longitudinal stability. For flight control he stipulated an elevator 'in a similar position to the tail in birds' and a rudder as components of the entirely adaptable tail unit on its universal joint, 'which effects the complete steerage of the vessel'.

Cayley propagated the virtues of dihedral wing-setting all his life, criticised Henson for not adopting this feature in Ariel, and himself used it to a (visually) striking degree in the twin-helicopter-convertiplane he was inspired to create after poaching Robert Taylor's design. On his 'boy-carrying' glider of 1849 and his man-carrier of 1852 he retained dihedrally set wings for automatic lateral stability and the

adjustable cruciform tail unit with tailplane and fins providing automatic longitudinal stability and directional stability. On the vital importance of these basic design factors he never faltered through half a century of aircraft construction. The tragedy was that nobody honoured him by reading and marking him until he was rediscovered as a dead prophet.

Tandem-winged with attractive dihedral, but still with negative flight control, Langley's Aerodrome A, Charles Manly up, falls at the first water-jump on the Potomac, 7 October 1903.

In 1871, 13 years after Cayley's death, a brilliant, young and frustrated Frenchman, Alphonse Pénaud, produced a working toy which was to have enormous impact on aeronautical design. (His frustration originated in the fact that, owing to bone tuberculosis, he could not be admitted to the French Navy, where his father served as an admiral. He committed suicide at the age of 30.) In 1870 he had constructed a successful model helicopter running on a twisted-rubber motor, which he had developed. He followed this up with a practical monoplane that was far more influential as a design than any of Cayley's detailed work and was probably, as image-forming propaganda, second only to the Aerial Steamer in promoting the psychological acceptance of the air age. This was the machine called the Planophore, a very graceful monoplane of 18in wing-span with a tapered mainplane and a diamond-shaped tailplane. It was driven, like Pénaud's previous helicopter, by twisted rubber.

It was demonstrated in the open air of the Tuileries gardens before the French Société de Navigation Aérienne in August 1871—a significant date, for it was shortly after the Siege of Paris during the Franco–Prussian war, when aerial transport and observation by balloon had proved of positive military value. Driven by an 8in pusher propeller placed at the aft extremity, the Planophore flew for a distance of 131ft in 11 seconds. The machine had maintained itself in the air, whatever the infectious merits of its rubber motor, because it was of very accomplished design. It was in fact the first inherently stable aeroplane to be submitted to the world. Its stability was provided laterally by the dihedral of the wing-tips, which were bent upwards both for the mainplane and the tailplane. Longitudinal stability came from the setting of the tailplane, which was raised in the rear to set it at eight degrees to the horizontal maintained by the mainplane.

Unconsciously Pénaud was duplicating the work of Cayley. Later, because he concentrated on the problem of stability, he rediscovered Cayley and unstintingly set up his genius as an incentive to other inventors. In his short career in aircraft design Pénaud made many brilliant suggestions, which, if he had lived, he might have seen realised in the air. The principal of lateral dihedral, which he had demonstrated as an invaluable aid for stability, had already been described by Cayley, who said, 'this most effectually prevents any rolling of the machine from side to side'.

Cayley's enunciation started with his strong argument against the use of the *reverse* of positive dihedral, the anhedral 'Aladdin's hat' shape of the parachutes of his day. Its application to condemn a purely horizontal single-surface mainplane, as in the Aerial Steamer, was a theoretical derivation. Briefly the theory is that if with an anhedral inclination of the wings the port wing dips, involuntarily as far as the pilot is concerned, 'it operates directly in opposition to the principle of stability; for the side that is required to fall [the starboard wing] resists [ie, lifts] much more in its new position [because it is now horizontal] and that which is required to rise resists much less'. But with a dihedral inclination, 'that side which is required to rise [the port side] has gained resistance by its new position [has more lifting capacity because it is now horizontal] and that which is required to sink has lost it [because the starboard wing is at a higher angle to the horizontal]'.

Pénaud also used *longitudinal dihedral*, a slight upward inclination in the angle formed by the chord-lines of the wings of the mainplane and tailplane, to reinforce longitudinal stability. Cayley's first model glider did in fact demonstrate negative longitudinal dihedral, a downward inclination of the projection of the chords of the mainplane and tailplane.

In a prophetic twin-propeller amphibious two-seater monoplane that Pénaud intricately designed and patented in 1876, but did not approach in full scale before his death, he included among many other forward-looking features steering air-brakes—movable sections of the wing designed to increase drag on one wing and therefore change the direction of the aircraft. This, though mooted more than once in other designs, was never incorporated in any aircraft constructed during the great surge at the end of the nineteenth century. What was more inspired was Pénaud's provision (within a glass-domed cockpit) of one control column that simultaneously operated the elevators and the rudder.

Ailerons were not then invented as movable surfaces designed to initiate roll, and therefore to control roll by starting contrary roll. In 1868 Matthew Boulton had patented a tentative aileron system that would have been highly destructive if it had ever been fitted to an aeroplane. Richard Harte had patented a more sophisticated system in 1870, stipulating flap-type ailerons on the trailing-edge of the mainplane of a fixed-wing tractor aeroplane, and that was a specification which in itself was remarkable for the age. However, Harte did not see the device as providing basic lateral stability—and since he had never flown, he had never experienced roll—but only as controlling the extra roll that he anticipated would be caused by propeller torque. In 1884 the Frenchman Alexandre Goupil designed a monoplane with opposite-acting ailerons, which were not, however, related to the action of the rudder. Many years were to pass before this automatic linkage simultaneously affecting rudder and wing surfaces—perhaps the most vital single factor in flight control—approached practical use.

If Alphonse Pénaud, 1850–1880, was a shooting star, his compatriot Victor Tatin, 1843–1913, was a stayer whose career spanned every phase of man's final soaring into flight yet could not notch one clear triumph. He was making rubber-driven ornithopters when Pénaud was producing his grand design of the amphibious monoplane. By 1879 he had produced a famous model monoplane, though not so graceful or influential as Pénaud's first success, which worked by compressed air. Between 1890 and 1897 he successfully tested a large twin (tandem)-screw monoplane driven by steam. In the next decade he became a Grand Old Man and cheer leader for the French aeroplane constructors in their rivalry with the Wrights. He sponsored an unsuccessful monoplane, the Tatin-De-La-Vaulx, in 1907, and a striking streamlined aircraft, the Tatin–Paulhan Aéro-Torpille, in 1911. Victor Tatin, very typical of the keen engineer who never bothered to abandon machinery for a sabbatical year and study actual flight, maintained an enthusiasm for 40 years yet never once saw any of his full-size machines achieve more than a hop before crashing.

In the meantime other designers pressed on with the application of their particular theories. D. S. Brown, a prominent member of the Aeronautical Society in England, was convinced that for longitudinal stability a tandem-wing configuration was essential, and he tested many monoplanes of this pattern in 1873 and 1874.

The American mathematician and astronomer Samuel Pierpont Langley, who began intensive work in aeronautics some 13 years later, read Brown's earlier reports and speculatively noted his enthusiasm for the tandem layout. Langley was also greatly influenced by the work of Pénaud, and he built around 40 rubber-driven model aircraft during the first years of his dynamic research. After 1892 he began to build steam-driven models, which he called aerodromes by mistaken etymology. When the first six models had failed to fly, he rebuilt the last two as tandem-wing models. In 1896 these became successively ready for launching, and they flew for 3,300ft and 4,200ft respectively at up to 25mph.

Two years later President McKinley instructed the United States War Department to commission Langley to build a man-carrying machine—the second Government sponsorship of aeronautics in history, Clément Ader having received his subsidy from the French in 1892. After prolonged failure to get an adequate engine, Langley's engineering assistant Charles Manly adapted a five-cylinder rotary engine produced by the automobile engineer Stephen Balzar into a five-cylinder radial engine, and improved its power from 8 to 52hp. A scaled-down version of this engine, installed in a quarter-size Langley tandem-wing monoplane, became historically the first petrol-engined aeroplane to fly. But, although it was tested in June 1901,

and could just about be said to have supported itself, it did not possess the longitudinal stability to sustain a horizontal flight path. By the time it came back from the drawing board to fly satisfactorily in August 1903 it was operating only four months ahead of the first *man-carrying* petrol-powered flight of the Wrights.

Meanwhile Langley and Manly were building a full-scale model of the tandem-winged commissioned craft Aerodrome A (see illustration, p. 81). It was put into the air two months after the delayed successful flight of the quarter-scale model, being launched by catapult from the top deck of a houseboat in the Potomac River. Langley thought he had got his theory all correct. He had longitudinal stability with his tandem wings and a Cayley-type cruciform tail unit. He had

Lawrence Hargrave's box-kite, invented in Australia in 1893, was belatedly seized on by many European constructors in the 1900s. The odd-looking aeroplanes that incorporated its cellular principle had undoubted stability.

lateral stability from the pronounced dihedral of the wings. But he had not given a thought to *flight control*, the actual mastery of the Aerodrome A within the element of air once it was launched.

Manly had volunteered to be the pilot. He considered that, since he could drive a motor car in two dimensions, he could consequently handle an aeroplane in three dimensions with no more trouble. (This was a common mistake among would-be pilots in 1903.) Manly had two control levers, one to work the rudder and one the elevator. He had never operated them at all in moving air, and was quite unaware that, since the rudder was not linked to the elevator and no one in America had yet dreamed up ailerons, he had only to turn the rudder significantly and the uncorrected airframe would dive straight into the Potomac. Perhaps, fortunately, Manly was never given a chance to test these deficiencies of flight control in Aerodrome A. As soon as he was catapulted from his launching float, he went straight into the river at 30mph without a chance to apply any rudder. Two months later the second launch produced a worse fiasco, with the aeroplane breaking up in the air; and, nine days before Orville Wright made the world's first powered, sustained and controlled flight in a petrol-driven aircraft, Professor Langley gave up aeronautics.

Parallel with this progressive disaster, another disciple of Pénaud and Brown, the Russo-Austrian Wilhelm Kress, had graduated over 20 years from making rubber-driven models to constructing a tandem-winged flying-boat powered by a 30hp Daimler engine driving twin propellers—one tractor, one pusher. Ready for test in 1901, the machine was the first full-size petrol-driven aeroplane ever built. Unfortunately it never took off. Running under power in the Tullner-bach reservoir, it was put into too sharp a turn, capsized, and was irretrievably wrecked.

Again over a parallel period, from 1882 until 1906, but isolated in distant Australia, Lawrence Hargrave had been working and lecturing on aeronautics in New South Wales. He, too, began by building rubber-driven models, and was for many years becalmed in the backwaters of the world of flapping ornithopters. But he was then 'converted' to steam, and in a further stretch of imagination began to research the aerodynamics of kites. He invented the box-kite, and made a kite-train strong enough to lift him off the ground. He began to design a man-carrying box-kite to be powered by a steam engine. Hargrave's box-kites unquestionably demonstrated longitudinal, lateral and directional stability, but he never developed the right power unit to raise them. After many years of experiment, during which he designed some 25 engines without having one take him off the ground, he decided that his finances would no longer allow him to continue full-time experimentation, and he erased himself from the record books. His work, however, was widely known and its influence was considerable. A Hargrave box-kite in tandem became the new characteristic configuration of a whole stream of biplanes in Europe, and the shape was visible in the first heavier-than-air machine to fly under power east of the Atlantic, in 1906, the year in which poor Hargrave dropped out of aeronautics.

Although Hargrave's great ambition had been to fly under power, and the later machines he was designing were box-kite aeroplanes, the first full-size machine he built, in 1894, was a tandem-wing mono-plane glider. It is a fair certainty that Hargrave, who even from Australia kept a very keen eye on aeronautical events in the rest of the world, built a glider because he had seen in 1894 a very widely published set of photographs of a man gliding.

Hargrave knew that man by reputation, and had followed his work with admiration; for he was the one man who had transcendentally justified the consistent courage of all the tower-jumpers whose bravery had seemed so futile in the past. He was the first man to cast himself into the air with wings, go back and fly again with equipment improved as the result of his experiences and positively advance the thinking and performance of the specialised world with his brilliant combination of theory and practice. He was the Prussian engineer Otto Lilienthal.

Although Lilienthal's achievement was always in hang-gliding—supporting himself by arms and elbows and letting his body swing to change the trim of his machine—he wanted eventually to fly, not soar. From the age of 21, in 1869, he had committed himself to the flapping ornithopter. He built fixed-wing gliders only to apprentice himself in the mastery of the air and the irregularities of the wind. To the same end he closely studied bird flight and the structure and shape of bird wings. He rediscovered the screwing action of the outer primary feathers by which the bird pulls itself forward and, perhaps impatiently, tried to duplicate this action with individual artificial feathers powered as propellers by a 2hp carbonic acid (compressed) gas motor. He was constantly building new machines, each one designed to possess improved stability.

In 1895 he decided to concentrate on biplane gliders, in which the required wing area, being nearer the longitudinal axis, was handier in control. But while he was actually gliding he could make relatively little adjustment—that is, coax little positive response from the machine in flight. He had a certain control over pitch by swinging his body backwards and forwards to alter the centre of gravity of the glider, and he countered roll by swinging his body to the side. He did build into his later machines an upwards-hingeing tailplane, and in the last days of his life he was working on a head harness by which he could mechanically lower this tailplane and use it in a limited fashion as an elevator. While testing this harness in flight, he stalled, side-slipped and crashed 50ft to the ground. On the following day, 10 August 1896, he died from the effects of a broken spine. The resigned expression he frequently used—*Opfer müssen gebracht werden* (Sacrifices must be made)—is carved on his tombstone.

Lilienthal had made great use of photography in his study of the flight of birds; and in turn many excellent photographs were made of Lilienthal in flight—a principal reason why he came so quickly to the attention of Hargrave in Australia and the Wright brothers in Ohio. Another man who admired, imitated, and positively developed his work was a British engineer, Percy Pilcher.

Pilcher had been a Royal Navy cadet at the age of 13, but retired at 19 to concentrate on engineering. When he was 27 he became assistant lecturer in Naval Architecture and Marine Engineering at Glasgow University. Almost immediately the current newspaper detail and photographs of Lilienthal's activities injected him with the fever to fly. He built one glider, the Bat, a monoplane with a vertical fin aft but no tailplane, the wings showing sharp dihedral; and during his summer vacation of 1895 he went to Lilienthal in Berlin in order to be taught to fly. He came back to test the Bat on the slopes of the Clyde valley and speedily followed Lilienthal's advice and added a tailplane for stability. In two subsequent models he increased the wing area and greatly mitigated the dihedral angle, which he had found was making his gliders almost unmanageable in strong winds; they plunged out of control before recovering stability from the effect of gusts. This seems a small point, but it is a very clear example of the application of experience to modify what had become to some designers almost a religious theory, mainly propagated because none of them had ever been called on to control an aeroplane with the stipulated dihedral.

In 1896 Pilcher came south to join Hiram Maxim, who had not yet wholly abandoned work on his biplane test-rig and had other plans in mind. In the summer of that year Pilcher built his best designed hang-glider, the Hawk, with cambered canopy wings having an area of 180 sq ft, undercarriage wheels braced by stiff spiral springs, and an attachment for a new towing technique for efficient take-off. In the same year Pilcher took out a patent for a powered flying machine with a 4hp petrol engine driving a pusher propeller. After failing to find a suitable engine, he began to build one. At the same time he set himself, in partnership with Maxim, to develop a projected helicopter; and still he continued to develop his gliding and modify his gliders. But on 2 October 1899 he died after falling 30ft in the Hawk during a towed take-off, when the sudden load imposed

Percy Sinclair Pilcher in flight with his best designed hang-glider, the Hawk, 1896. The undercarriage wheels are not too clearly evident in this picture. Pilcher's best flight in this machine was 250yd, and he died when it crashed in 1899.

The Flight of Birds as the Basis for the Art of Flying was the theoretical work published by Otto Lilienthal in which he published his rediscovery of the fact ignored since Cayley had demonstrated it, that the outer primary feathers of a bird's wings screw into the forward air and achieve the onward drive in flying. Lilienthal duplicated these outer primaries—there are six in each wing—and intended to activate them as individual airscrews by a small portable gas engine. (He was professionally a specialist in light steam engines.) But in this picture the contraption is being used solely as a hang-glider. Lilienthal eventually favoured the biplane glider as giving the required lift with more manageable control, and the second picture, artistically a most evocative composition, explains some of the great influence he exerted in presenting the grace and release of soaring flight.

by two horses over-active on the tow-rope broke up the tail unit of the machine.

Lilienthal and Pilcher, indisputable pioneers and clear flying enthusiasts whose appetites grew by what they fed on, had worked in their short careers on the immediate problems of flight control. With one exception they were unique in this preoccupation, because no other experimenter was flying, dealing at first hand with 'the irregularities of the wind'. Undoubtedly they were right to work their way towards eventual powered flight by the stepping-stone of unpowered gliders. Possibly, in their concentration, they did not do as much work as they might have done on the design features of craft stability, and this is an omission particularly notable as neglect from P. Sinclair Pilcher, naval architect. But within three weeks of Lilienthal's death and throughout Pilcher's three last active years, another man had begun to build and continued to test gliders with the declared object of evolving a machine with 'automatic equilibrium', the familiar goal of inherent stability. This was Octave Chanute, a French-born railway engineer domiciled in (though not confining himself to) the United States, who was 64 years of age when he tested by proxy his most

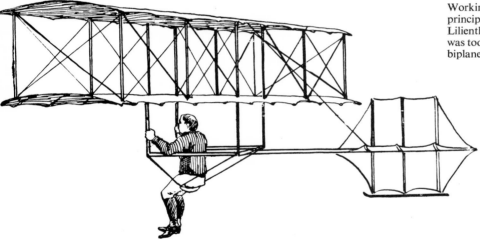

Working at the same time and on the same principle of the mastery of flight control as Lilienthal and Pilcher, Octave Chanute was too old at 64 to go aloft himself in this biplane hang-glider built in 1896.

significant biplane hang-glider in 1896.

Chanute had made himself the encyclopedist of aeronautics. The cream of what every designer needed to know lapped through the pages of his classic compilation *Progress in Flying Machines*, published in 1894. In 1900 Chanute met the Wright brothers, at their request, and he became their stimulator, sounding-board and propagandist. His inspiration was in the sphere of morale rather than practical innovation. The only physical features the Wrights took over from him in their machines were the secure trussed bracing of their biplane wings and the seed of their method of assisted take-off. But Chanute took the configuration of the Lilienthal-type biplane glider as far as it could go before moving control surfaces were introduced by the Wrights.

Wilbur and Orville Wright, aged 32 and 28 respectively in 1899 when they began to study aeronautics seriously, were the sons of a bishop of the United Brethren Church living in Dayton, Ohio. They had built up a modest business success in selling, and later making, cycles. By that time they had been attracted by the exploits of Lilienthal and had closely studied the flight of birds. In 1899 they acquired, among other works whose titles they had requested from the Smithsonian Institution in Washington, Chanute's great summary of the technical progress of aeronautics, and in August of that year they built a biplane kite.

Its wing-span was only 5ft, but it demonstrated from the start the most significant feature of their innovation in aircraft control—the system of *wing-warping*. This is an inaccurate expression that history has saddled us with. It means that they twisted screw-wise the extremities of the wings to alter the angle made by the wing-tips to the wind, and so *control roll* caused by currents of unstable air. The increase of resistance (or lift) at one wing-tip and the diminution of lift at the other would induce the machine to return to the horizontal, or to bank. It was a system whereby the pilot—not yet 'flying by the seat of his pants', because the Wrights began by flying in a prone position—developed an intuitive reaction to what was happening to the machine and an increasingly speedy correction of its attitude by

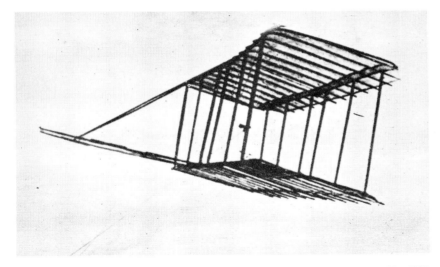

The Wrights' No 1 glider, 1900, being flown as a tethered kite, the wing-warping not being adjustable in flight. What they called the 'horizontal rudder'—the horizontal adjustable forward elevator—is not obvious because of the angle of the photograph.

The Wrights' No 2 glider of 1901 had an anhedral droop to the wings and the pilot lay in a hip cradle by which he controlled wing-warping.

mechanical means, which were also improving.

From the outset the Wrights were defying the mainstream of European thought, which decreed the construction of an inherently stable aeroplane. Only the glider pilots Lilienthal, Pilcher and Chanute—and Le Bris in his albatross craft of 1857 and 1868—had previously rejected this trend. The Wrights sought to build inherently unstable aircraft demanding from the pilot continuous control in flight. Wilbur was uncompromising about this 'fundamentally different principle'. Their resolve, he said, was that 'we would arrange the machine so that it would not tend to right itself'.

Their small-scale biplane kite of 1899 was succeeded by their No 1 glider in 1900. This had fixed biplane wings with a span of 17ft and a horizontal plane braced *forward* of the wings to act as elevator and to protect the pilot in nose-dive crashes. This elevator moved up and down automatically as the glider changed its fore-and-aft attitude. The wing-warping could be adjusted only from the ground, not during flight. After very few flights the original dihedral wing-setting was cancelled, and with that step the Wrights abandoned all formal automatic stability. Like Pilcher, they had found the effect of the lateral dihedral too extreme to master in strong irregular gusting wind.

In 1901 they constructed their No 2 glider, with the wings, cambered after trials to a new curvature of 1 in 19, measuring roughly

22ft by 6ft 6in, giving an area of 290sq ft, and having a slight anhedral droop. They had now fashioned a hip-cradle in which the pilot lay face down, and, by turning his body to right or left, he could warp the wings. This machine was tested with fair success near the Kill Devil sandhills, south of Kitty Hawk in North Carolina, where there was fairly constant strong wind and soft sandy landing. The glider was launched by being run by hand into a strong wind, the two ground staff holding the wing-tips.

After intensive redesign in 1902, which included wind-tunnel research to test aerofoil sections, the Wrights built their No 3 glider, with reduced wing camber, maintained anhedral droop, and a slightly increased wing-span to 32ft, giving with decreased chord an area of 305sq ft. Initially they had a fixed double fin at the rear, but after some disastrous spins they replaced this with a movable single rudder, its controls always linked to the warp-cradle so that it invariably turned in the direction of bank. With this vital innovation the brothers made up to 1,000 controlled glides in the autumn of 1902

The launching technique for the Wright gliders, in this case their No 3 of 1902 after modification that substituted a single rear rudder for the previous two fixed fins.

The Wrights' powered aeroplane, Flyer No 1, with Wilbur Wright in the hip-cradle, shows the chain drives, crossed on the left for counter-rotation, which reduced the pusher propeller speeds in relation to engine speed.

and became highly experienced pilots. They once noted without rancour that during five years of experimental gliding Otto Lilienthal had been airborne for little more than five hours; it seems that they logged at least half this flying time during five weeks in 1902 alone, with a maximum glide of over 200yd in 26 seconds.

Wilbur and Orville Wright now set themselves to the construction of a powered machine. After failing to find an automobile engine of suitably light weight, they entirely adapted the engine they had built for their wind-tunnel, and they designed and built, with their mechanic C. Taylor, a four-cylinder, 4in by 4in bore and stroke, petrol-driven engine weighing 179lb dry weight with the magneto, and giving 12hp before pre-heating of the inlet air reduced it to 9hp. The engine's 1,090rpm were reduced by chain drive to run two counter-rotating pusher propellers, which were also designed by the Wrights.

They installed this engine in their newly designed Flyer No 1, a 1 in 20 cambered biplane of 40ft 4in span, and 510sq ft wing area, with a double elevator forward and a double rudder aft. The machine was launched from a wheeled truck set on a 60ft carrying rail laid into the wind, the wing-tips being supported by ground staff.

On 17 December 1903 this rail was laid on level ground at Kill Devil and the Wright brothers, piloting in turn, made four flights against a wind of about 25mph. The fourth flight, with Wilbur in the cradle, covered 852ft and lasted 59 seconds. The Wright brothers had 'done it' four and a half years after, as enthusiastic innocents, they had written to the Smithsonian for a reading list on aeronautics.

In 1904, using the Flyer II—basically the same design as Flyer I but with an improved engine giving some 16hp—the Wrights flew on 80 experimental flights and developed a system of accelerated take-off. This required a tall derrick suspending a heavy weight on a rope, which, with pulley connections, eventually ran along the starting track and doubled back to the aeroplane. When the weight dropped, the Flyer II—and every subsequent Wright machine until 1910, when they belatedly changed from skids to wheels—was pulled forward at speed for take-off.

The assisted take-off was originally introduced because of the diminutive 'airfield' they were now using, the so-called Huffman's Prairie, a 300-acre meadow near Dayton. The main ultimate virtue of this patch was that it forced the Wrights into volatile manoeuvrability. Wilbur's five-minute flight of 9 November 1904 took him four times round the prairie!

But the tight turns which were necessary emphasised a recurring tendency to stall. In 1905, with their new machine Flyer III, the Wrights deliberately unlinked the irrevocable connection between warping and rudder movement. Warping had two objectives: to change direction and to counter roll. Rudder movement was necessary in turning but counter-productive when warping was being used to correct lateral instability caused by gusting wind.

Thus, in the great confrontation of opposing schools crying and decrying the slogan of stability, the Wrights made their final point for constant pilot control. Having immeasurably improved equili-

Orville Wright, the pilot in this historic picture, taken at 10.35am, Thursday, 17 December 1903, claimed this 12-second flight as 'the first in the history of the world in which a machine carrying a man had raised itself by its own power into the air in full flight, had sailed forward without reduction of speed, and had finally landed at a point as high as that from which it started'.

The shape in the sky which proclaimed that practical flying had been achieved: the Wrights' Flyer III, with wing-span 40ft 6in and area 503sq ft, the wings cambered 1 in 20 and set flat, without dihedral or anhedral, biplane forward elevator and twin rudders, new propellers and the tested 16hp Wright engine. The flight photographed here took place on 19 September 1905. In the next modification of Flyer III the hip-cradle was abandoned, the pilot sat upright and there was a second seat, and rudder and wing-warping were controlled by hand levers and cables.

brium in flight by abandoning reliance on architecture but rigidly linking roll and rudder, they modified their practice into a much more conscious, even less automatic, fluency of control. If their hip-cradle governing warp and rudder had been capable of construction and operation with a universal joint, like the joystick of the future, they might never have needed to disconnect the wires. They now began to fly, fully aware of the relation between warp and rudder, with free controls and the steadily increasing knowledge of their most effective coordination.

15 THE FINESSE OF WING CONSTRUCTION

In 1901, as has been mentioned, the Wrights began detailed testing of aerofoil shapes in their own wind-tunnel. The first work in this sphere, as in so many others, had been done by Cayley, who used a whirling arm to investigate the lifting effect of both camber and the angle of incidence of aerofoil and air, and who additionally analysed the wing sections of birds he had shot. The first wind-tunnel was built in England in 1871 by John Browning and Francis Wenham, a marine engineer and a naval architect, who made a detailed study of cambered wings. Earlier Wenham had tested full-size gliders with wings in five parallel planes shaped according to his theories. Although he may have got his aerofoils right, he was only too keenly aware of the disadvantage of having no engine. 'When the wind approaches 15 or 20mph', he lamented, 'the lifting power of these arrangements is all that is required . . . but the capricious nature of the ground-currents is a perpetual source of trouble. In a dead calm, it is almost impracticable to get sufficient horizontal speed, by mere running alone, to raise the weight of the body.'

In 1875 a serious young English engineer, Horatio Phillips, then only 20 years old, had been experimenting with hydrofoils and took out a patent on them. He turned to aerofoils, and devised a new wind-tunnel to test them, inducing by steam injection a much steadier airflow than Wenham's fan-generated currents. By 1884 he had registered patents on six double-surface aerofoil sections of varying gradation and camber, intended to shape curved wings for aircraft.

The first 'Venetian blind' multiplane test-rig of Horatio Phillips, constructed in 1893, ran on a circular track and showed good powers of lift, but not enough longitudinal balance to take the machine in a steady ascent from the ground. Forty aerofoils, 19ft long, were designed to a shape that Phillips had patented.

Phillips laid down the theory that increased camber on the top of a double-surface wing creates the suction of reduced pressure above, and gives lift. Later he refined the shape of his double-surface aerofoils to flatten the lower part of the leading-edge into a bi-convex shape designed to diminish drag and increase lift. He went on to build both models and full-size aircraft based on his corollary that *superimposed* aerofoils of his design, constructed with high aspect ratio (ie, long and narrow) would provide admirable lift. From this assertion there came the famous 'Venetian blind'—not Phillips's term, but everybody else's for his multiplane of 1893, an erection of no less than 40 aerofoils 19ft long and 1½in chord, set vertically behind a 6ft 6in tractor propeller in a wheeled frame on a circular track over 100yd round.

This test-rig did rather worse than Hiram Maxim's, which was being operated about the same time. At 40mph the rear wheel of the tricycle dolly lifted 3ft but the front wheels stayed earthbound. But a similar rig on a 200yd circuit lifted almost 400lb. In 1904, when the light petrol engine was more advanced, Horatio Phillips put a pilot aboard a similar machine, free-running this time, though with only 20 cambered aerofoils. But, although again the lift was good, the balance was wrong and the multiplane had poor longitudinal stability. In 1907 the indefatigable Phillips, now aged 62, put four banks of 48 aerofoils in tandem behind a 7ft propeller driven by a 20hp engine; and there is good ground for believing his report that it lifted off the ground of Streatham Common for 500ft—which would make it the first powered aeroplane ever to be flown in Great Britain, beating Samuel Franklin Cody's performance at Farnborough in 1908 by over a year.

Phillips continued to design, though no longer to build, his individualist aeroplanes. But his theoretical work on the aerodynamic properties of aerofoils was confirmed and enlarged in the first decade of the twentieth century by F. W. Lanchester of England, G. H. Bryan of Wales, and Ludwig Prandtl of Germany. As a quartet of individual thinkers, these men laid the foundations of aerodynamic theory, which influenced all ensuing aircraft design and construction.

The Phillips multiplane of 1907 may well
have been the first British powered aircraft
to fly.

16 ENDEARING CHARMS... DEAR RUINS

The evolution of flight was effected through experiments that failed as well as those which succeeded. Failures gave information, either to the pioneers concerned or to their professional rivals, closely observing. Fly, hop or crash, the grotesque aircraft clamouring at the sphincter of the birth of flight were serious engineering projects in spite of their apparent crudity. But piety can also afford the grace to smile, if only it has charity enough not to guffaw. Every freak was someone's baby. All made a contribution to the cause. Some inspired aircraft failed because they were the last twig on a particular limb of growth, but in their final agonies they served a purpose in dissuading designers from launching into any more thin air on their side of the prairie. Some pointed out with a dying finger the one missing specification, now glaringly obvious, which was essential for glory. In the long run every machine, even the very best, went 'back to the drawing board' at some time, because science and skills had advanced, and a better best was now possible.

The history of aviation exacts a sense of wonder, a sense of justice, a sense of humour, and a world of affection. As Tom Moore once wrote, and the pipes and drums of the Irish Guards later made into their most moving lament:

> Believe me, if all those endearing young charms
>   Which I gaze on so fondly today
> Were to change by tomorrow and fleet in my arms
>   Like fairy gifts fading away,
> Thou wouldst still be adored as this moment thou art,
>   Let thy loveliness fade as it will,
> And around the dear ruin each wish of my heart
>   Would entwine itself verdantly still.

Affection must be acknowledged. The endearing charms of a landscape littered with other men's follies deserve their due recognition. If we concede that they are now grotesque antiquities, we may well see no shame in proclaiming them as dear ruins about which the heart entwines.

Captain Ferdinand Ferber, of the French Artillery, was 36 years old when Otto Lilienthal was killed, and he alone in France, with Pilcher in England, had the understanding, the ambition and the youth to consider powered flight within his personal reach. In 1901 he built a Lilienthal-type hang-glider and began jumping off 20ft-high scaffolding to practise with it. But at the end of that year, through correspondence with Chanute, he learned of the work of the Wrights and built a Wright-type glider, basing his design on photographs Chanute had sent him. But he did not comprehend either the theory or the practice of the Wrights concerning control in roll, and did not incorporate wing-warping. His slightly improved version of his original glider, built in 1903, had two wing-tip rudders—affording him in reality no extra control—but he was so over-confident after soaring in it that he declared he was now ready to install a motor. His powered version of this Wright-type glider was a complete failure. During the next year, 1904, he recast his thinking and decided to aim for inherent stability by adding a tailplane to his design. When this picture of Ferber flying in his new machine was published in 1905, it had great influence in swinging European designers towards the Wright-type *configuration* of aeroplane, but in combination with the 'old-world' reversion to attempted inherent stability. As a 'mood' picture this conveys most seductively the exhilaration of flight. It will be judged that the flapping wing-tip rudders were giving Ferber no more control than a couple of burgees.

Before maturing as an outstanding theoretician of space flight (as early as 1912), Esnault-Pelterie had progressed from gliding to build some effective unconventional aircraft like this REP2 of 1908—which, curiously, had no ailerons but used a primitive form of wing-warping.

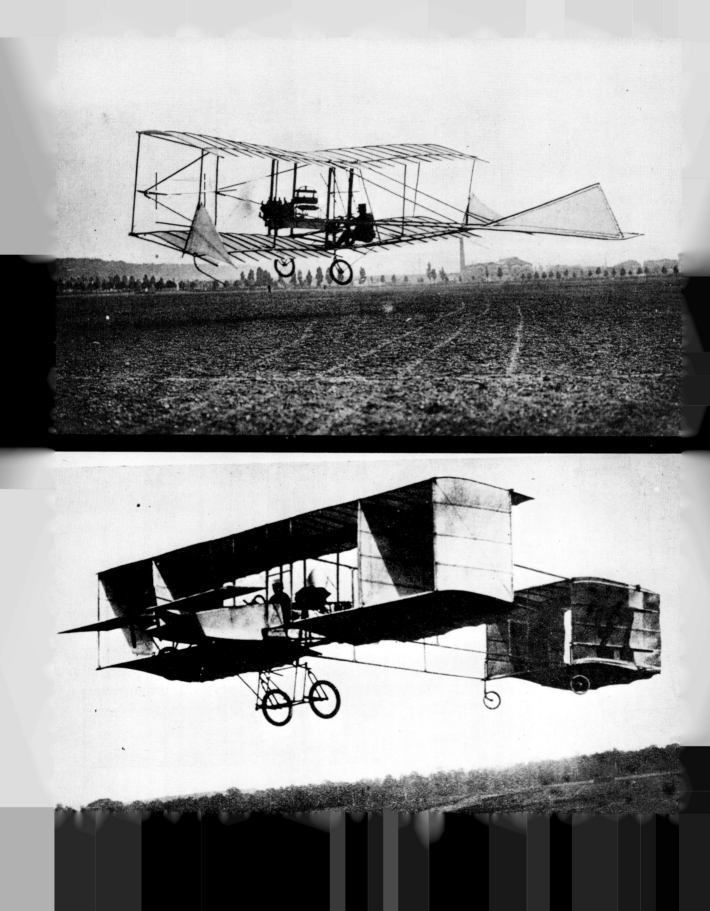

Ferdinand Ferber, though always pluckily trying to design a winner, never succeeded in building a powered aeroplane that did more than hop, and when in desperation he bought a Standard Voisin in 1909, he hit a ditch at speed between a landing and a second take-off at Boulogne, and was killed.

Léon Levavasseur, first an artist then a designer of the Antoinette engine, which he named after the daughter of his partner Jules Gastambide, put the first Antoinette driving two four-bladed propellers in a large monoplane, which he designed in the shape of a bird and tested unsuccessfully in 1903. Levavasseur retired to develop his engine in racing motorboats. He came back to aeronautics in 1908 when he designed the Gastambide-Mengin I which crash-landed after eight days of trial— quite a normal life for an aircraft of that period. But this was developed into the Antoinette series of aeroplanes, which confirmed Levavasseur's position as a brilliant designer of pure aircraft as well as of engines.

The Standard Voisin pusher biplane seen here, a box-kite construction with front elevators and side-curtains to aid its already formidable stability, was the unexciting all-purpose 'Ford Model T' of the air for some years. But it was overdue back at the drawing board because of its then retrogressive design. It was very easy to fly so long as the pilot wanted only to go in a straight line.

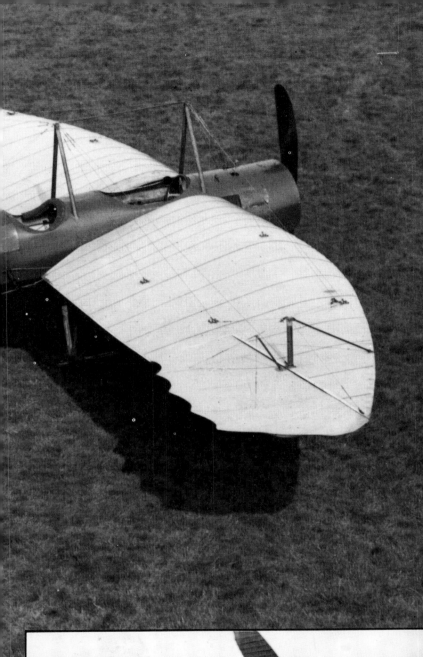

Another artist—the Alsatian José Weiss, who was domiciled in England—showed heartening understanding of the properties of the aerofoil in this thickening bird-wing model glider, *far left*, which he exhibited in 1905. Weiss was later snapped up by Sir Frederick Handley-Page to design his company's early machine. (*Left*) the HP1 Bluebird monoplane which Weiss designed. Weiss's swept-back wing were a feature of the Handley-Page Yellow Peril (*above*) of 1911.

The first Europeans to fly for more than a minute's duration were Henry Farman on 9 November 1907 and Léon Delagrange on 11 April 1908. These triumphs took place at the military exercise ground, the *Champ de Manoeuvres*, at Issy, on the Seine near Paris. Issy was the first nominated aerodrome in history, although it had to double as a hippodrome—for the pioneer fliers had to take turns with the French cavalry, who practised formation-charging over the same ground. Among the many struggling enthusiasts who were booking time at Issy was the tempestuous Louis Blériot, who eventually hauled himself up to stay aloft for over eight minutes on 6 July 1908. All these intoxicating exploits were achieved five years after the Wrights first flew at the Kill Devil Hills. But it is fair to say that not only was the American pioneering being practised thousands of miles away from the traditional centre, but also the Wrights dramatically stopped flying for almost three years after early October 1905. Apart from the American Glenn Curtiss and the Canadian James McCurdy,

The Pischoff I biplane of 1907, though not quite a flyer, set the style of future biplanes with its clean configuration, uncluttered by forward control areas or box-kite cellules, its Chauvière Intégrale tractor propeller making it what is now regarded as the first in Europe of a modern design. The tail unit was a Cayley-type cruciform union of tailplane, fin, elevator and rudder. There were no ailerons, no wing-warping, and consequently no pilot-operated lateral control. The Pischoff I introduced the famous Anzani engine into aeronautics.

who were in action when the Wrights came out of their cocoon in the late summer of 1908, *the only constant work on flying*—the waking dreams, the designing, the construction, the testing and the sickening failures—was being done in Europe, mainly in France. Some of these last still-births, before the actual delivery of man in free flight, have therefore a special interest, for often they present the vestigial features of their lineal successors that actually flew.

Alfred de Pischoff drove out to Issy in 1907 and 1908 to test what was then a revolutionary biplane he had had built in the workshops of Lucien Chauvière. It had wings of unequal span, the upper wing being longer. There was nothing of the box-kite about it. There was an open configuration about this machine, and the floating tail went back even to Cayley. This was the first full-scale biplane with a tractor propeller, and Chauvière had improved on the warped canoe-paddles that were used up to that time—and well beyond that time in England—and had produced the first 'sophisticated' airscrew used in Europe. Pischoff's aircraft had no forward control surfaces, and in appearance it set the standard for the new look of a whole generation

Louis Breguet's biplane, the Breguet I, clearly derived from the Pischoff I, had a tractor propeller, wings of unequal span, twin rear rudders, and wing-warping for both lateral control and elevation. The machine was very influential because it received much attention, on the ground, at the great formative Reims Aviation Week of 1909. Its actual performance at the Reims meeting was not so distinguished. While Henry Farman was flying 180km in his biplane, the Breguet made three short flights of which the maximum distance was 500m, and it crash-landed after being airborne for 300m on the last attempt.

Alberto Santos-Dumont's 14-bis in flight on 23 October 1906, the first considerable and witnessed aeroplane flight in Europe. The machine, which is going from left to right in the picture, had pronounced dihedral box-kite wings with an area of 52sq m. A 25hp Antoinette engine originally drove a 2½m diameter pusher propeller at 900rpm, but for this, its second free flight, a 50hp Antoinette was substituted. The forward box-elevator pivoted vertically. Santos-Dumont is standing in a wicker basket and he is wearing a body-harness which in the following month he adapted to control octagonal ailerons between the wing-tips, leaning to right or left to establish some lateral control. In this finally-modified 14-bis he made a record flight of 220m, but crashed the next time he took the machine up. That was the end of the 14-bis —typical of the short life of aircraft types in the 1900s.

of practical biplanes. But the unsavoury truth about this machine was that in itself it was not exactly practical. Its best flight at Issy was a hop of 7m in December 1907.

Nevertheless it was the direct inspiration of the Breguet I biplane of 1909, which in turn, although it notched little achievement itself, stamped a silhouette for biplane configuration through the next decade. In the year between the launching of the two classic biplanes of de Pischoff and Louis Breguet, 1908, de Pischoff abandoned the biplane concept to build a tandem monoplane harking straight back to Langley, with three sets of wings of diminishing span, and an elevator and rudder brought well forward, though still behind the tractor propeller. This machine was swiftly abandoned, and its fate is an instance of the speed with which the designers tentatively grasped and speedily relinquished their fleeting ideas of configuration: everything was fluid, nothing was jelled into conventional form by previously proven ability, and therefore most new machines were unconventional. Indeed, the solitary performance of the de Pischoff tandem monoplane was as good as the Breguet I's best—a 40-second hop of 500m.

The jolliest of all the daring young men whose career spanned the

birth of flight was Alberto Santos-Dumont. He was the son of a
wealthy Brazilian coffee planter, on whose vast estate Santos was
driving railway engines at the age of 10. He came to Paris in 1891,
when he was 18, to study the development of the automobile. But he
swiftly developed a passion for aeronautics and, as inventor and
patron, he was an inspiring pioneer of flight in machines both lighter
and heavier than air. He first took up ballooning in 1897, and went
on to build airships. He was the first to put the internal combustion
engine into the air as a practical instrument. By 1901, at the age of
28, he had won fame and the then gigantic prize of 125,000 francs by
navigating his Airship No 6 from Saint-Cloud, around the Eiffel
Tower, and back again—the first really guided flight by air. Santos-
Dumont captured the affections of the Parisians by flying his airship
very low (and quietly) down the Paris boulevards, and surprising
strollers by unexpectedly joining in their conversation as he passed
them from the rear. He used to tie his airship up at his country club
as a cowboy would hitch his horse to a rail.

Santos-Dumont subsequently went to America, learned from
Chanute of the achievement of the Wrights, and enthusiastically came
back to France to concentrate on heavier-than-air flying. He built his

The first popular light aircraft, Santos-Dumont's *Demoiselle* in 1909, at Issy. The designer had utilised an effective Chauvière propeller and the machine's top speed was 90km per hour. The wingspan was 10sq m. The cruciform tail unit, acting as rudder and elevator, was fixed by a universal joint, operated by handlever. Lateral control was through wing-warping operated by a rocking lever strapped to the (sitting) pilot's waist.

famous 14-bis canard-type cellular biplane, which he first tested from an overhead wire rope ineffectively pulled by a trotting donkey, and later (see illustration, p. 108) suspended from his Airship No 14. In free flight in this machine he first hopped 60m on 23 October 1906, and later 220m in 21·2 seconds on 12 November 1906, and won the prize offered by the Aéro-Club de France for the first heavier-than-air machine to fly for over 100m.

Santos-Dumont soon abandoned biplanes and the canard-type configuration. In 1907 he built his No 19 light monoplane, weighing only 110kg, which he modified in 1908 and from which finally grew his definitive *Demoiselle* (Dragonfly), the No 20 of 1909, a sporting machine weighing 143kg. In the following year he fell a victim to disseminated sclerosis and was forced out of aeronautics, though he survived helplessly until 1932.

At Billancourt, a mile away from Issy on the other side of the Seine, the brothers Charles and Gabriel Voisin had set up the world's first aircraft factory, where they developed their own rather pedestrian designs, but, much more importantly, coped with all comers by fulfilling individual orders. Among their clients were the friendly rivals Henry Farman and Léon Delagrange.

Henry Farman, whose father had settled in Paris as a newspaper correspondent, was of British nationality, though he could speak no English. He did not take French nationality until 1937, and he survived until 1958, when he was 84. He was trained as an art student—an extraordinary number of early pilots and aircraft designers were artists—but he abandoned art, first for cycle racing and then for automobile racing, winning the heavy car class of the great Paris–Vienna race of 1902 in a 70hp Panhard. In 1907, at the age of 33, he was 'converted' to aeronautics, and commissioned from the Voisin brothers one of the stock biplanes they were then producing. (They had filched the design from an inaccurate diagram of the Wright machine of 1903.) This had box-kite configuration of wings and tail unit, with pusher propeller and forward elevator. Farman speedily modified this, and by November 1907 he had achieved a

A prize of 50,000 francs went to Henry Farman for the execution, on 13 January 1908, of the first kilometre return-to-base flight in Europe, achieved in his Voisin-Farman I (mod) biplane. Since Farman was not to adopt lateral control for another 9 months he could make no sharp turn and, once past the starting pylon, he had to fly in a banked attitude following a steady circle throughout.

flight of over a minute. After further modification he flew the Voisin–Farman I (mod) on the first half-kilometre-and-back (*Kilomètre bouclé*, or kilometre return-to-base) accomplished in Europe, at Issy on 13 January 1908. Léon Delagrange, flying a machine with very similar progressive modifications, the Voisin–Delagrange II and III, accomplished in the first six months of 1908 flights that gradually improved to a 14km stretch done in $18\frac{1}{2}$ minutes. Farman maintained a parallel progression.

This miniscule rivalry between the courageous and inventive—but, in some aspects of technique, almost wilfully blind—fliers in France was transformed between August and December 1908 by the arrival at Le Mans of Wilbur Wright. The Wright brothers had gone into utter hibernation, as far as practical flight was concerned, between October 1905 and May 1908. They had applied for a patent for their machines that was slow in being granted. In the meantime they tried to influence, in respective order, the Governments of the United States, Great Britain and France, into purchasing the rights on their aeroplanes. They offered a package deal in the sense that negotiations should be all or nothing—the take-over of the rights on the trusted testimony of the brothers without detailed prior examination of the machines—since they feared rejection of the offer after adequate commercial spying on their exclusive features. All these negotiations were at first unsuccessful. The Wrights therefore closed down all flying, though they successively improved their engine and perfected

Having modified his previous modification to produce the Voisin-Farman I-bis (mod) with four side-curtains between the wings, and putting up a creditable 40km flight with this adaptation, Henry Farman 'saw the light' regarding lateral control, which was making the flying of Wilbur Wright the envy of all French airmen, and he installed four broad wing-tip ailerons in his revised model, the Voisin-Farman I-bis (2nd mod). Later he used neater ailerons in his first 'signed' aircraft, the classic Henry Farman III.

The Goupy I triplane, built by the Voisins to the design of Ambroise Goupy, had a wing-span of 7½m and a weight, including its eight-cylinder 50hp Renault engine, of 500kg. Its best performance under test in 1908 at Issy was a hop of 150m, but it inspired other designers.

Wilbur Wright's first public flight in France in August 1908, at Hunandières, near Le Mans, before he transferred to the neighbouring military camp at Auvours. This Wright A, the 1908 refinement of the 1905 Flyer III, was the model used by Orville and Wilbur Wright for their demonstrations to the Governments of the United States and France of the potentialities of flight à la Wright. The A-type was a two-seater pusher biplane with wing-span of 41ft, chord 6.5ft, area 510sq ft, forward elevator area 70sq ft, powered by a Wright four-cylinder 30hp engine driving twin propellers at 420rpm, and attaining a speed of up to 40mph. It was launched by the Wright's peculiar 'derrick-and-weight' method, illustrated here at Auvours.

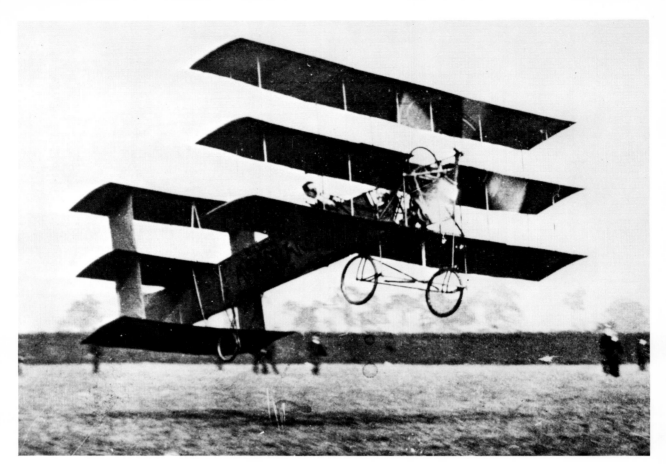

The Roe II triplane of 1909, called contemporarily the Bullseye and built after its designer (later Sir Alliott Verdon Roe of AVRO) had seen drawings of the Goupy I, marks a typical sequence in the 'back to the drawing board' aspect of aeronautical progress. The Roe II flew for 300yd with a 9hp JAP engine driving a tractor propeller whose revolutions were reduced by gearing in the Wright manner. Then it crashed on Hackney Marshes. Roe picked himself out of the wreckage, pulled the peak of his cap to the front, and went back to other triplanes, some of which also crashed. The Roe III is illustrated The last of them was the Roe IV of 1911, distinguishable among other features by its monoplane tail, and very much taken to the heart of the British public.

their Flyer III into a standard two-seater—and pilot and passenger now literally sat instead of sprawling—which is now known as the Wright A. This impasse was broken in 1908 when satisfactory business arrangements were made with both the United States and the French Governments. Then, while Orville Wright demonstrated the Wright A at Fort Myer, Washington, DC, Wilbur Wright travelled to France, assembled his machine at the Léon Bollée factory near Le Mans, and finally demonstrated it over four and a half months, principally flying from the military Camp d'Auvours near Le Mans.

Altogether Wilbur Wright put in some 26 flying hours in this protracted exhibition. It was an undisputed triumph. The French had until that moment never really trusted the reports that the Wrights had flown between 1903 and 1905, and the subsequent long inactivity supported their suspicion. Now every aeronautical enthusiast in Europe, after the incredulous reports of the first day's flying, strained to make the trip to Auvours, and all were struck with wonder and enthusiasm at the apparently effortless and intricate flying that they witnessed. They had never seen, and scarcely thought possible, such technical achievement as the efficiency of engine and propeller, and such individual mastery of flight control as Wright was exhibiting in his nonchalant climbing, banking and turning—accomplished, as the Europeans now accepted, by the unique linkage of warp and rudder.

It was in this realisation of a visible revolution in the art and

science of flying that Henry Farman reapplied himself to design in the autumn of 1908. He had already made further modifications to his machine, and had achieved a flight of 40km. But, as he now saw only too well, the aeroplane flew clumsily, the pilot was continually stretched at exhausting tension to maintain stability, and the turns on rudder only were ludicrously imprecise as the machine yawed wildly off course. Farman then made his most radical change.

He realised the impossibility of continuing to fly successfully without any lateral control, always the *bête noire* of European machines. Since he could not take over the closely patented Wright system of wing-warping to control roll, he installed in his machine—designated now by historians the Voisin–Farman I-bis (second modification)—the world's first (moderately) successful ailerons. They were enormous—some 2m broad in a wing-span of $10\frac{1}{2}$m—downward-moving hinged surfaces at both upper and lower wing-tips. With this drastically modified machine he had introduced sufficient control to carry out what was the first genuine cross-country flight in history, from Bouy to Reims, 27km in 20 minutes. He also achieved what was then said to be the world altitude record—at 25m—although in fact Orville Wright had already flown at 310ft (96m). But on 18 December 1908 Wilbur Wright, flying in France, took the official record by flying at 360ft.

Farman then, in a somewhat feverish pursuit of experimental

change, built a shorter canopy-wing over the boxed mainplanes and flew the machine as a triplane. The triplane had been a feature in the mental landscape of aeronautical designers since John Stringfellow's well known model of 1868, and this itself was based on a far more seriously designed and tested 1843 triplane of Cayley's, which was then less familiar. Moreover, there was already a triplane flying from Issy. It was a short-span (7½m) tractor-propeller 'three-decker' with side curtains enclosing the mainplanes and a box-kite biplane tail with the elevator in the middle of the box and a rudder projecting behind. It had been built by the Voisin brothers to the design of

This replica of the cuddly Roe IV was built for the film *Those Magnificent Men in Their Flying Machines*, and still flies under the aegis of the Shuttleworth Collection at Old Warden, Bedfordshire.

Ambroise Goupy. Though the Goupy I (it was followed by an influential biplane, the Goupy II) did get off the ground for a not exactly stupendous distance, its greatest impact was that, through advance descriptions of it printed in England, it inspired the Englishman A. V. Roe to build a much more effective series of triplanes that even today, two-thirds of a century later, provide one of the immortal mascots of aeronautics; and its replica is still flying. But when the Goupy I first hopped in September 1908, no one in Britain had ever yet flown an aeroplane. On this side of the Atlantic the delivery ward was still located at Issy.

In the middle of 1910 the British War Office offered the use of a wide area of Salisbury Plain, near the Royal Artillery's Larkhill and within thirsty motorcycling reach of the pub-strewn old coach-stage of Amesbury, to anyone seriously experimenting in flying. The first to take up the offer was Sir George White, who had recently founded the British and Colonial Aeroplane Company, better known by its later name of Bristol Aircraft. Later in that year the War Office indicated that Salisbury Plain would be the headquarters of an Aeroplane Corps, which would come under the Officer Commanding the Balloon Corps at Aldershot. Soon a few officers in the Royal Engineers were quietly testing machines in the line of duty, and a consortium of army pilots parked in White's hangar on the Plain an old

banger of a Blériot that they privately owned and had nicknamed the Man Killer because of its unpredictable behaviour. The centre grew, and when in April 1912 Lord Haldane, the War Minister, and Mr Winston Churchill, First Lord of the Admiralty, announced the formation of the Royal Flying Corps, with separate military and naval wings, they confirmed that the Central Flying School would be located at Upavon, on another part of Salisbury Plain.

This inauguration of a military aeronautical arm occurred only three and a half years after the first acknowledged power flight in Britain (since, even accepting that Horatio Phillips got his 'Venetian blind' airborne at Streatham Common, nobody influential knew about it), and only three years after the first British pilot, J. T. C.

British Army Aeroplane No 1, flown by S. F. Cody to his great surprise as the first aeroplane to fly in Great Britain, had a Wright-type biplane configuration, but ran on a wheeled undercarriage and required no assisted take-off. There were forward elevators and a rear rudder. Cody also fitted between-wing ailerons. A 40–50hp Antoinette engine drove two pusher propellers.

The first British aircraft to fly under power: the Army's *Nulli Secundus* airship, 120ft long with a 50hp Antoinette engine and a Cody-designed tail unit, which he afterwards detached and used as a petrol-engined power glider. The airship generated enormous public enthusiasm when, on 5 October 1907, it was flown from Farnborough to circle the dome of St Paul's Cathedral in London. But, after a 50-mile flight lasting 3 hours 25 minutes, it had not the power to return against a freshening breeze. The airship never flew again in this form, but was reconstructed, with a new Cody tail unit and a lighter streamlined keel, as *Nulli Secundus II*. But the modified airship made only two flights and was scrapped in September 1908. The German opposition, the Zeppelins, were already approaching a length of 400ft. The scrapping of *Nulli Secundus II* in September was the only reason why British Army Aeroplane No 1 flew in October; for research funds were so low that there was only one engine between the two aircraft, and Cody re-installed the Antoinette in his biplane.

Moore-Brabazon, flew in Great Britain. It was an astonishingly swift and confident military acceptance of flight, as if the Royal Tank Corps had been formed in 1898, three years after the first British motorists had ventured to drive, at a limit of 2mph in the town and 4mph in the country.

After the death of Percy Pilcher in the glider Hawk in 1899, flying within Great Britain was extinguished. The only interest in aeronautics of any aspect displayed by the Government was in the use of observation balloons, and later of man-lifting kites intended to be used for the same purpose, which Captain Fletcher Baden-Powell (the brother of the future Chief Scout), then of the Scots Guards, demonstrated in 1894. Baden-Powell swiftly became secretary, and later president, of the Aeronautical Society—not yet 'Royal'. In 1903 he competed at the society's first International Kite Competition on the Sussex Downs, at which the military representatives of five governments were present.

Among the competitors here was Samuel Franklin Cody, the American owner and very skilful star of a travelling Wild West show based in England. Cody had become interested in box-kites after the visit to England of the Australian Lawrence Hargrave in 1899. Having a flair for publicity, he sailed across the English Channel to Dover in December 1903 under the power of three skilfully manipulated kites. This exploit was performed just a few days before the first engine-powered, sustained and controlled flights in history were achieved by the Wright brothers at the Kill Devil Hills. Early in 1904 Cody and his sons Leon and Vivian were engaged as civilian contractors to build man-lifting observation kites for the Army's Balloon Factory at Farnborough. The Officer Commanding the Balloon Section at Aldershot, Lieutenant-Colonel John E. Capper, gave active sponsorship to the Cody project in addition to stimulating enthusiasm for the construction of an army airship. Later in 1904 Capper went over to the United States and interviewed the Wrights. He reported back to the British War Office that England was 'very backward' in the development of flying machines, that 'America is leading the way whilst in England practically nothing is being done'.

The only substantial work then in progress was, in fact, the private experimentation with model gliders and small rubber-driven aeroplanes being carried out by the 27-year-old engineering draughtsman A. V. Roe, and the construction of a remarkably stable tail-less monoplane with broad swept-back wings by Lieutenant John W. Dunne of the Wiltshire Regiment. Capper met Dunne and encouraged him. Cody meanwhile was transforming his kites into bird-wing gliders of which the culmination was an extremely light biplane glider of 51ft wing-span and 8ft chord, which weighed only 116lb. Many soldiers were trained to fly this, tethered like a kite, but eventually young Vivian Cody, piloting it in free flight, got out of control and crashed badly. S. F. Cody then promptly decided to concentrate on powered flight, and lobbied the War Ministry for funds to develop it.

In 1906 J. W. Dunne, now invalided from the Army as a captain on half-pay, joined the Balloon Factory under Colonel Capper, now its superintendent but still also Commandant of the Balloon School. Dunne had a secret brief to develop a tail-less arrowhead powered aeroplane. In the same year A. V. Roe, now jobless but almost frenetically orientated towards powered flight, vainly sought a position on the staff of the Balloon Command, the only aeronautical specialists in Great Britain. Rejected, his only consolation was to win a *Daily Mail* competition for powered model aeroplanes with a biplane of 9ft upper wing-span driven by 1lb of twisted rubber.

At Farnborough S. F. Cody was now Chief Kiting Instructor at the Balloon School, but he was also working on a power plant and stabilising wings for a projected airship. His son Vivian, after a year in hospital, was superintending the manufacture of man-lifting kites. And in a secluded enclave of the airship hangar Dunne was developing a tail-less monoplane as well as a biplane glider. In the autumn of 1907 the Dunne machines were tested, without outstanding success. Meanwhile Cody, as engineer supervising a 50hp Antoinette engine he had acquired from Léon Levavasseur, with Capper at the helm and Captain W. A. de C. King, Royal Engineers, as navigator, flew the new airship *Nulli Secundus* from Farnborough to London and

The Dunne D5 twin-propeller pusher tail-less biplane of 1910 was powered by a 60hp Green engine driving propellers 7ft in diameter. It took a crew of two in a boat-shaped nacelle. It was the culmination of a long series of experiments by J. W. Dunne on tail-less aircraft, and led on much later to modern delta-wing designs. Demonstrating that it fulfilled his design objective of extreme stability, Dunne (who was not officially allowed to fly as a pilot because of a heart condition) took the machine up with Orville Wright's patent agent aboard, and flew it 'hands off' while he wrote out specification details on a scribbling pad.

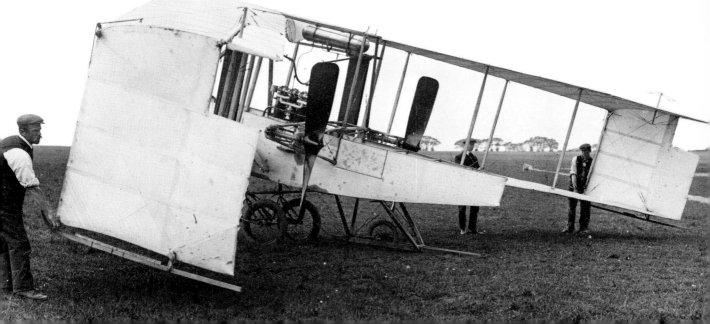

round the dome of St Paul's. Then the wind freshened to a greater speed than the airship's 16mph maximum could counter, and it was moored in the middle of the cycle track at Crystal Palace. Later Cody used the discarded stability-wings from *Nulli Secundus* to construct the first powered glider that ever flew in England; one flight at Farnborough was of 4½ minutes' duration. From this project he went on to construct a variation of the biplane glider, a large Wright-type twin-propeller biplane designated British Army Aeroplane No 1 (in spite of the fact that the prototype of Dunne's machine had been commissioned a year earlier).

Roe in the meantime had used his *Daily Mail* prize money to take a hut at Brooklands motor-racing track in which he built an unsuccessful full-sized petrol-powered biplane, the Avroplane. And a new British aeroplane manufacturer was in the field. Short Brothers, a balloon construction firm run from under some Battersea railway arches by Eustace and Oswald Short, and patronised by the War

Office and the Hon Charles Rolls, was commissioned by J. T. C. Moore-Brabazon to build him a glider. 'Brab', soon to be Britain's first pilot, housed his machine at Brooklands in a shed next to Roe's, and set about converting it to power with an engine bought from the Voisin brothers. A. V. Roe had sent to Paris for a 24hp Antoinette to replace the ineffective 9hp JAP engine he had installed in his biplane. Charles Rolls, abandoning ballooning and determined to tackle power-flying by first mastering the art of gliding, commissioned a glider from Short Brothers—now reinforced by a third, eldest, brother, Horace. By this time Dunne was at Blair Atholl testing his powered biplane D4, still tail-less but with twin engines.

Roe claimed that he hopped in June 1908, when towed by an automobile at Brooklands; but research shows that he had an assisted take-off by running (backwards, in relation to the stream of the track) down the steep Members' Hill beyond the finishing straight. Horatio Phillips has been given more credibility for his claim to have

The De Havilland II, the aeroplane which Geoffrey de Havilland successfully launched in 1910, and which successfully launched him on his career as designer, test pilot, and constructor. When Sir Geoffrey died in 1965 at the age of 83 his ashes were scattered, by his request, over the airfield at Beacon Hill near Newbury, where the man who had built the DH4, the Moth, the Mosquito, the Vampire and the Comet had tested and flown his original practical aircraft.

been airborne in 1907, but the feat was not published at the time and had no effect on design development.

On 16 October 1908 S. F. Cody got British Army Aeroplane No 1 indisputably into the air and fairly indisputably into the first significant flight in Great Britain. But it was more by luck than judgement, and ended in accident, as is shown by Colonel Capper's report to the War Office of that date, a document still to be seen in the Science Museum in London:

> Mr Cody has been running the machine about on a good many occasions in order to get its balance, but he was instructed to attempt nothing sensational or any long flight but as soon as he was sure that he could really fly he was to let me know with a view to our having a proper power trial. The machine has left the ground for short runs, at a height of one or two feet, on several occasions.
>
> This morning Mr Cody took the machine out as usual, and ran it up a slight slope on to a plateau, near the Farnborough road; to his surprise it lifted off the ground for about 50 yards when going up this hill but he did not seem to attach much importance to this. He ran along the plateau and down the slope as usual, when to his astonishment the machine went to a considerable height in the air. He tried to bring it down but he states the front plane [ie, the Wright-type forward elevator] is not big enough to bring it down sufficiently quickly when once it has got up and, seeing in front of him a clump of trees, decided to try and clear them. However, another clump of trees beyond looked so forbidding that he thought it appropriate to turn to the left and try to come down on a piece of ground. He was, I should estimate, at a height of 16–20 feet above the ground at the time. He turned, gradually sinking all the time. The left wing tilted down and struck the ground hard, crumpling up the tips. Then of course the machine turned round and fell on its nose.

The estimated distance of flight was 1,390ft and the speed between 25 and 30mph.

By the next year, 1909, Roe had abandoned his biplanes and progressed to the more successful triplanes, which have been previously illustrated (p. 119). By 1910 Dunne's tail-less D5 was flying well, and the firm of Handley-Page was in business. At the end of this year Geoffrey de Havilland, having built and flown a good machine, became aircraft designer and test pilot to the Army Aircraft establishment at Farnborough; and, alongside the artillery ranges and overlooking Boscombe Down, where the great aeronautical experimentation of the future was to be done, British military flying was being established on Salisbury Plain.

19 WESTERN AERIAL EXPERIMENT

In the United States there was a sphere of endeavour outside the charmed circle of the Wrights. The pioneer inspiration for flight had come within America from Samuel P. Langley, whose continuous experiment, discussion and enthusiasm started with work on a massive whirling arm in 1887 and finished pathetically with the collapse into the waters of the Potomac of the catapulted tandem monoplane Aerodrome A, on 8 December 1903, only nine days before the Wrights first flew. Langley retired in disgust at the unjustified disgrace with which he was smothered by public opinion, led principally by politicians. The Wrights took no part in this despicable hounding campaign. When Langley died in despair in 1906 at the age of 72, Wilbur Wright said: 'The fact that the great scientist, Professor Langley, believed in flying machines was one thing that encouraged us to begin studies.'

Another pioneer, also known as 'Professor' but with less academic backing than Langley (Santa Clara College, California against the American Naval Academy and the Smithsonian), was John J. Montgomery, who had built three gliders even before Langley turned to aeronautics, but was not such a consistent prophet. In 1905 Montgomery built in California a tandem glider that was launched from a balloon, and the parachute jumper D. Maloney, engaged to pilot the machine, crashed and was killed. Montgomery, though not a young man, continued to experiment with gliders, and in 1911 he crashed and was killed in one of his own machines at the age of 53.

After Langley's death a fresh consortium of American enthusiasts came together as the Aerial Experiment Association at Hammondsport, NY. They designed and constructed a number of machines— biplanes with Wright-type forward elevators and a variety of tail units. The distinguishing visual feature of these biplanes was a dihedral lower wing and anhedral upper wing, so that all AEA aeroplanes display mainplanes shaped like crossbows twinned, with the bow-strings between the wings. Their distinguished mechanical feature was the 30–40hp air-cooled engine built by Glenn H. Curtiss.

Red Wing, first of the American AEA series sponsored by the Aerial Experiment Association, was designed by Lieutenant Thomas E. Selfridge and flew on 12 March 1908, only 6 months before Selfridge died —the first casualty in history as a result of powered flight—when Orville Wright, piloting with Selfridge as passenger, saw his machine break up around him at Fort Myer on 17 September 1908. Red Wing, like its immediate successors, had a 30–40hp Curtiss air-cooled V-8 engine. It is seen fitted with skids for take-off from the ice-bound surface of Lake Keuka, NY. F. W. Baldwin, who took it up for a flight of 319ft, was the first Canadian ever to fly. Like the mayfly, Red Wing had a life of less than a day. When it crash-landed after its second flight, it was abandoned after the engine had been salvaged—an unplanned and undesired obsolescence that was accepted philosophically by the early pioneers.

Curtiss, aged 29 in 1907, was already the fastest man in the world, having ridden a motorcycle over a measured mile at 136·3mph in that year. He was a specialist in engines, and was then running a motorcycle and engine factory. The first AEA machine, Red Wing, was designed by Lieutenant Thomas E. Selfridge and tested in March 1908 from the ice-bound surface of Lake Keuka. At the first take-off, piloted by the Canadian F. W. Baldwin, it was airborne for just over 100yd. At the second it crashed, and no more work was done on it.

Instead, Baldwin designed a successor called White Wing, replacing the skids installed in the first machine with landing wheels, and incorporating small ailerons. Flying two months after Red Wing, it achieved a soaring distance of 1,000ft but again crash-landed. Curtiss then built, with the speed characteristic of those days, a third machine, June Bug, and on 4 July 1908 he won a trophy offered by the magazine *Scientific American* for the first public and officially measured flight of over a kilometre. Seven weeks later it was coaxed to fly for

June Bug, designed by Glenn Curtiss for the AEA series, and piloted by Curtiss in this photograph, was flying within a month of the crash of its predecessor and eventually achieved a 2-mile flight on 29 August 1908. The characteristic bowed effect of the mainplanes is visible. June Bug had a biplane tail unit and four triangular wing-tip ailerons. The Wrights promptly accused Curtiss of infringing their wing-warping patents with his ailerons, and the bitter legal wrangle went on for years.

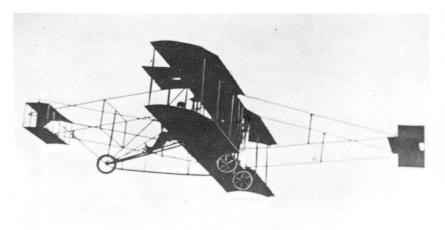

Golden Flier, the Curtiss machine designed independently of the AEA, and flown in the spring and summer of 1909, had flat unbowed biplane wings with substantial between-wing ailerons—Curtiss' interim effort to avoid any suggestion of infringing the Wrights' warp-wing patent.

two miles, and it also achieved one circular flight.

At this stage in the fellowship of the AEA one of its members, Tom Selfridge, was killed when riding as passenger to Orville Wright during the acceptance trials for the United States Army of the Wright A. Curtiss himself was at the mild beginnings of an increasingly bitter feud with the Wrights, who claimed, with incomprehensible selfishness as it now seems, that the triangular wing-tip ailerons Curtiss was using were an infringement of their patent on wing-warping. Curtiss's alternate pilot in June Bug, the Canadian James A. D. McMurdy, designed the next AEA machine, Silver Dart, an enlarged version of June Bug with similar wing-tip ailerons and (after modification) incorporating both a forward and a rear rudder. Using a 50hp Curtiss engine, McMurdy flew this machine for half a mile over the ice of Baddeck Bay, Nova Scotia, on 23 February 1909, registering the first flight ever in Canada.

Curtiss then formed the Herring–Curtiss Aeroplane Company and, abandoning the crossbow configuration, built a square flat-winged biplane with oblong ailerons between the wings, the Golden Flier, in which in July 1909 he flew 24·7 miles nonstop. At the same time he was building a modification of this machine with a Curtiss 50hp engine, which he entered for the great Reims Air Week of August 1909, and which scored some notable successes. Glenn Curtiss then went on to concentrate on seaplanes, an early sporting specimen of which has already been illustrated (p. 77), and to pioneer air operations to and from United States Navy vessels—making the cruisers *Birmingham* and *Pennsylvania* the first aircraft carriers in history by his experiments early in 1911. Curtiss seaplanes were supplied to the Royal Naval Air Service in World War I. They were the only American machines to go into combat, for after the United States entered the war in 1917, all the aircraft used by the United States Air Service were either British or French.

20 BLÉRIOT AND THE FRENCH CIRCUS

The Blériot VII of 1907, a classic-styled
cantilever monoplane, increased Blériot's
airborne record to 500m.

Louis Blériot, a shrewd, enthusiastic, practical and not overpoweringly intellectual man of enterprise, is a fair example of the men who
bulldozed aeronautics into moderately profitable business in the first
decade of the twentieth century and who, 'because they were there',
deservedly made their fortunes and simultaneously speeded the progress of flying incalculably when the Great War hit the world during
the next decade. Blériot, at the age of 29, was experimenting in the
first year of the new century with a model ornithopter. He was
comfortably in business as an optical engineer manufacturing acetylene lamps for automobiles and searchlights. By 1905 he had commissioned from the Voisin brothers a float-plane glider, which Voisin
called the Voisin–Blériot and Blériot listed as the Blériot II, the next
in line after his bird-flapping model. This machine, which was similar
in appearance to the Voisin–Archdeacon but incorporated a number
of Blériot's personal suggestions, came to grief speedily during its
towed take-off on the Seine, and nearly drowned Gabriel Voisin,
who was at the meagre controls. Blériot next ordered from Voisin
a float-plane of striking design, in effect a tandem biplane with no
tail, the biplanes boxed, and the whole configuration rounded in to
an aspect of an ellipse.

This machine, powered by a 24hp Antoinette engine driving two
tractor propellers, never rose from the Lac d'Enghien where it was
tested, and Blériot spent much of 1906 in modifying its structure and
adapting it as a land-plane. But both the Blériot III and the Blériot
IV failed to rise.

In 1907 Blériot built three aeroplanes, all vastly different from his
past machines—they were now all monoplanes—but also widely
differing from each other. This is an indication of the uncertain state
of design in Europe, where no power-pilot had been off the ground
for a longer time than the 21·2 seconds recognised for Santos-
Dumont.

One of the versions of the Blériot VIII with pivoted wing-tip elevons.

The Blériot XI (mod) of 1909, with the characteristic open fuselage adopted by the designer at this time, was the first machine in Europe to achieve efficient lateral control by the application of wing-warping. In this machine Blériot made his historic flight across the English Channel.

It was the shape of Santos-Dumont's canard 14-bis that Blériot first turned to. He constructed the Blériot V, a romantic craft of the flying duck configuration as far as head and neck were concerned, but with baroque circling wings more like those of a courting swan than a lean, streamlined, migrating duck. The Blériot V made four take-offs, and at least got into the record books for having airlifted Blériot for a distance of 6m. But it crashed and was wrecked. Blériot immediately built his Langley-type tandem monoplane Blériot VI *Libellule* (the Dragonfly), which has been illustrated (p. 44), with pivoted wing-tip elevons used mainly as elevators. The *Libellule* made progress for Blériot. On the Issy trial ground it finally lifted for 184m, but, at the end of this idyllic 17-second float, Blériot was brought to earth with a thud as the machine crash-landed and had to be written off. Within six weeks Blériot was afield at Issy in a totally different machine, a classic tractor monoplane. Its mainplane could have come from the old Aerial Steamer except that it was dihedrally set and not belayed to king-posts, but cantilevered—Blériot's VI and VII were pioneer cantilever monoplanes. There was no tailplane, but broad double elevons too narrowly closed in on a deep rudder. With a 50hp Antoinette driving, the four-bladed metal propeller pulled the

A watery end to Hubert Latham's attempt to fly across the Channel in his Antoinette IV on 19 July 1909, 6 days before Blériot's successful flight. The Cayley-Henson type 'kite' tail unit and the Henson king-posts are clearly visible.

machine aloft at Issy for a top distance of 500m in 45 seconds. Blériot was slowly going ahead.

He spent the first half of 1908 building the Blériot VIII, a monoplane which, in various versions, was largely the test-bed for his further success. During the second half of the year he not only achieved a celebrated cross-country journey of 28km, but designed and completed three more machines, which he exhibited at the Paris Motor Show in December. The Blériot VIII-bis—probably the most promising modification, though he revised it later—had large downward-moving flaps as ailerons. The Blériot IX monoplane had a 16-

In 1897 Lawrence Hargrave originated the rotary engine, in which the crankshaft is fixed and the radially placed cylinders and the crankcase revolve, carrying the propeller. Laurent Seguin developed the rotary aero-engine in 1907, and its first significant use was at the Reims Air Week of 1909, when Henry Farman fitted the seven-cylinder 50hp Gnome into his biplane III. Rotary engines, cooled by their own movement in the air, dispensed with the heavy water-cooling systems and radiators previously necessary, and at one stroke reduced the weight-per-horse-power ratio from about 10lb to about 3lb. The Gnome, in various versions with *Le Rhône*, dominated powered flight through World War I, and the castor oil they scattered liberally and indiscriminately accounted for the black smudges on the face of the typical pilot of that war.

cylinder 100hp Antoinette engine driving a four-bladed propeller, but some design fault barred it from lifting and it was abandoned. The Blériot X, a three-seater biplane, never moved once after its showy installation in the exhibition hall of the Grand Palais de Paris. The Blériot XI, which was tested alternately with the IX at Issy, was eventually a winner, after several modifications, which gave it a new engine—a three-cylinder 25hp Anzani—and a new propeller, a Chauvière Intégrale revving at 1,400rpm, and, at last in Europe, an efficient lateral control system through the successful use of wing-warping.

In this Blériot XI (mod) the persistent pilot won the *Daily Mail's* prize for the first flight across the English Channel, taking $36\frac{1}{2}$ minutes for a $23\frac{1}{2}$-mile flight in the calm dawn of Sunday, 25 July 1909. It was a chancy effort, but it came off. Six days earlier a much better equipped competitor, Hubert Latham in his Antoinette IV, the strong Henson-type braced monoplane (see illustration, p. 134) had set off, but his usually reliable 50hp Antoinette engine had failed, and he had had to ditch, to be rescued by the French destroyer *Harpon*. Five weeks later Latham's Antoinette IV (which was fitted with ailerons) took on the Blériot XI at the Reims Air Week, and flew 154km nonstop to take second prize in the Grand Prix. Latham's Antoinette VII (which used wing-warping) took the altitude prize with 155m at the same meeting and notched 68·9km per hour to finish second in the sustained speed event.

The Reims Air Week—*La Grande Semaine d'Aviation de la Champagne*—which was held from Sunday to Sunday, 22–29 August 1909, was, with Blériot's flight across the Channel, the outward and visible sign that flight was now accepted as an inescapable feature of the social and political scene. Blériot's dawn arrival had signalled an inevitable decline in the potential of British sea power. Many political and military leaders went to Reims, including the British Chancellor, David Lloyd George, who publicly confessed 'Flying machines are no longer toys and dreams'. The actual performances registered were breathtaking even by comparison with the previous year. The maximum distance flown nonstop was 180km by Henry Farman, using the then revolutionary Gnome rotary engine in his Henry Farman III (mod). The top sustained speed record was taken by Glenn Curtiss with 75km per hour. The grace and manoeuvrability of the three Wright Type A machines were a revelation in flight control.

Blériot won the sprint speed record at 76·95km per hour in the Blériot XII, a two-seater tractor monoplane—the first passenger-carrier in Europe—which on the last day of the show crashed on landing and was burnt out, though Blériot escaped relatively unharmed. Louis Blériot had by now little need of the publicity given by the Reims meeting. His flight across the Channel had resulted in immediate orders for 100 Type XIs. Even in this age of fast development a modified Blériot XI was a popular trainer in the Royal Flying Corps of 1914. Later during the war the Blériot firm merged with Deperdussin and made the SPAD, the most notable French fighter from 1916 onwards and the fighting vehicle of many American pilots.

21 THE LONGEST ASCENT

Paul Cornu's experimental powered helicopter was the first to raise a man (marginally) on 13 November 1909.

Nothing has crashed back to the drawing board more often, more dispiritingly, and for longer periods of knockout coma than the helicopter. It was a (string-pulled) practical toy eight centuries ago. Leonardo da Vinci saw its practical possibilities nearly five centuries ago. Sir George Cayley reactivated it and later virtually created bi-plane design in 'conventional' aircraft by his brilliant presentation of the double-rotor convertiplane he had borrowed without acknow-ledgement from Robert Taylor. In the nineteenth century helicopters were designed (but never worked full-size) with power plants relying on foot-pedals, gunpowder, rubber, clockwork, compressed air, steam, internal combustion and gas turbines. At last, in 1907, Louis Breguet, then a 27-year-old engineer at Douai, assisted by Professor Charles Richet, built a 'gyroplane', the Breguet–Richet I, with twin eight-bladed rotors, which on 29 September 1907 lifted itself and its one-man crew—together weighing 12½cwt, and needing some cautious steadying from witnesses present—and on one occasion travelled 100yd and upset its helpless pilot into a beetroot field. Later that year, on 13 November, Paul Cornu of Lisieux constructed a much

J C H Ellehammer, the often under-rated
Danish pioneer, with his helicopter in
1912. The craft lifted from the ground but
failed to fly.

The first undisputedly successful helicopter, the German Focke-Achgelis Fw 61 of 1936, had a 160hp Siemens-Halske Sh14A seven-cylinder radial engine driving twin three-blade rotors mounted on outriggers. It weighed about a ton. The cut-down propeller in the nose did not propel but merely cooled the engine.

139

The Sikorsky VS-300 saw the end of the beginning of the long development of this type of single-rotor machine.

lighter twin-rotor helicopter, which, using a 24hp Antoinette engine, lifted Monsieur Cornu 1ft into the air. Because it required no steadying assistance from lookers-on, the Cornu machine ranks as the world's first practical helicopter.

However, both machines subsided to the ground and rose no more. Three years later a Breguet–Richet II was built at Douai, and marginally worked. But it was destroyed during a hurricane in the following spring. In the same year Igor Sikorsky was experimenting in Russia with a helicopter but, failing to find the power to lift a man as well as the machine, he abandoned the project for 20 years.

In 1912 J. C. H. Ellehammer also raised himself a few inches off the ground, using the system of cyclic pitch control, which was further developed in the years after World War I by the Argentinian Marquis de P. Pescara in machines built in Europe. From 1923 the Spanish Juan de la Cierva, mainly working in England, was developing his Autogiro, which required rotor blades to lift and a conventional tractor propeller to drive horizontally.

Slow progress in helicopters proper was made, and by the mid-thirties the machine had at its best flown over a kilometre in distance and 17m in height. In 1935 Louis Breguet, who had been designing more successful aircraft during the 26-year interval, built another helicopter, this time with a twin-coaxial rotor, and flew in it over 44km on a closed circuit, reaching a height of 158m. But in 1936 the German machine Focke-Achgelis Fw 61 nearly doubled the distance and achieved an altitude of 3,427m. This prototype was developed into the Fa 223, which went into production in Germany in 1940.

Igor Sikorsky, who in the long interval since 1910 had emigrated to America and designed, among other aircraft, a successful series of flying-boats, had returned to the consideration of his first dream in 1930. On 14 September 1939 he lifted himself off the ground in his prototype VS-300, a single-rotor machine. From that moment of exhilaration the conception was well and truly aloft, and Sikorsky machines have been prominent in every modern development of the helicopter.

22 GREATNESS THRUST UPON THEM

The system of jet propulsion for aircraft was first seriously suggested in 1783, but in application to balloons. Joseph Montgolfier, the designer of the pioneer *Montgolfière*, thought that sufficient reaction for forward movement could be obtained by opening a vent in the sector of the balloon that was to be nominated as its rear. A trial run was planned, but owing to other technical defects the balloon could not get off the ground even to start the experiment, and it was torn to pieces by a Paris mob that had become bored with waiting for scientific progress.

Jet propulsion of aeroplanes was put forward with much technical backing from the last third of the nineteenth century. The suggested

Sir Frank Whittle's Whittle W1 Turbojet of 1941, which was installed in the Gloster E 28/39 (seen in the Science Museum above it), was put to its first test flight on 15 May 1941. The engine produced 850lb thrust for a dry weight of 560lb.

The Gloster E28/39, which was the vehicle testing the Whittle jet engine. On its original flights (from Cranwell) it reached 338mph at 15,000ft. Later, with a 1,700lb Power Jets st W2/500 engine, it reached 450mph.

propellants included petrol vapour, steam, compressed air, a combustible gas–air mixture and other variants. By 1908 there was a well argued proposal for a high-speed aircraft that should not only be driven by jet reaction but should have the ram-jets hinged to allow for vertical take-off. In 1910 Henri Coanda, a 23-year-old Rumanian who was star pupil at the Paris School of Aeronautics, built a sesquiplane (a biplane with the lower wing markedly shorter than the upper) powered by a four-cylinder 50hp Clerget engine that drove a centrifugal compressor providing a 485lb thrust—of air, not of a mixture of fuel and air. Coanda, who later became a designer for Bristol Aeroplanes, described graphically how he had taken off in this machine—quite inadvertently, since he did not then know how to fly.

Even in the days of World War I aircraft research workers were considering gas turbines as a source of power. A gas turbine takes in air into a compressor, burns it with fuel, and uses the force of the burning gas either to drive a propeller—which is how the Great War scientists envisaged the operation—or to create jet thrust by being directed away through a narrow nozzle—which is how Frank Whittle

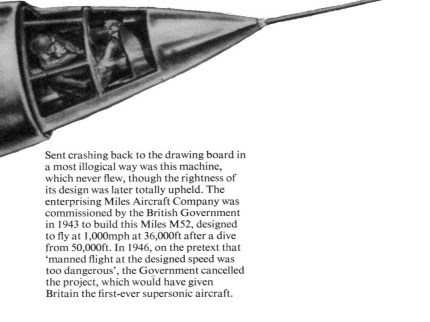

Sent crashing back to the drawing board in a most illogical way was this machine, which never flew, though the rightness of its design was later totally upheld. The enterprising Miles Aircraft Company was commissioned by the British Government in 1943 to build this Miles M52, designed to fly at 1,000mph at 36,000ft after a dive from 50,000ft. In 1946, on the pretext that 'manned flight at the designed speed was too dangerous', the Government cancelled the project, which would have given Britain the first-ever supersonic aircraft.

wanted it. Eleven years after he had first patented his idea and gone dutifully back to routine work in the Royal Air Force, Whittle saw an experimental machine, the Gloster E28/39, take off on the first test flight of a British jet. The outcome was the formation in 1944 of squadrons of Gloster Meteor twin-engined jet fighters powered by Rolls-Royce W2B/23 Welland Series 1 turbojet engines. The Mark I, which could fly at 420mph at 30,000ft, achieved fame by shooting down numbers of the V1 flying bombs. The Gloster Meteor III, the more considerable wartime version, had Rolls-Royce Derwent engines that pushed the speed to 490mph.

Meanwhile, totally unknown to the British, the Heinkel He 178, a petrol-burning jet monoplane designed by Pabst von Ohain apparently without deep reference to Whittle's patent, had first flown a week before the outbreak of World War II, to inaugurate the jet age at 700km (435 miles) per hour. Culpably slow development of the jet principle in Germany led eventually to the appearance in operations of the Messerschmitt Me 262, twin-engined with a maximum speed

The American Bell X-1, physically similar to the Miles M52, but air-launched and rocket-propelled, first achieved supersonic flight on 14 October 1946 when it reached 670mph at 42,000ft—that is, Mach 1.015. Later modifications were the X-1A and X-1B. The X-1A achieved Mach 2.42 in 1954.

of 870km (541 miles) per hour at 6,000m, of which some 300 fought in the closing stages of the war.

Before the launch of either the Meteor or the Me 262, the Miles Aircraft Company in England had accepted an official commission in 1943 to deliver a jet-propelled aeroplane to fly at 1,000mph at 36,000ft. Early in 1946, when there was a prospect of the first prototype being tested within the year, the project was cancelled by the British Government, which pleaded an incredibly flimsy excuse. The design was later completely justified by the satisfactory performance of later models made by Vickers. Great Britain lost the lead won by her scientists, and the first supersonic aeroplane was the American Bell X-1, a rocket-powered air-launched machine with design characteristics astonishingly similar to those of the slaughtered Miles M52. The Fairey Delta 2 gained the official record as the first aircraft launched from the ground to exceed 1,000mph in 1956.

The civilian exploitation of jet propulsion by the British led to the triumph and tragedy that were welded into the fabric of the De

The Comet I inaugurated for BOAC the world's first passenger jet services, but sadly pioneered the discovery of unsuspected metal fatigue caused by the stresses of constant changes of pressure.

147

Havilland Comet I. The aircraft was bravely and intelligently designed years before the crest of the wave of development, which it did in fact surmount. It launched the world's first passenger jet services, maintained by BOAC when the British airline was at the height of its prestige. The flying time on all world routes except the transatlantic, which was beyond the range of Comet I, was halved by its then amazing speed of 490mph at 35,000ft in very smooth flight above cloud turbulence. Then, one after another, three machines broke up in the air and over 100 deaths were registered. The machine was withdrawn from service in 1954 after a span of less than two years in operation. There followed a prolonged and intensive scientific examination of the parts of the aircraft dredged from the depths of the ocean, which altogether took four years. The result of this investigation was the virtual 'discovery' of a metal fatigue, hitherto unsuspected, caused by the continuous succession of increasing and decreasing the pressure of the cabin structure as the jet flew up to altitudes 'above the weather' and came down to land. The deaths of the innocent Comet passengers were the price paid to save the lives of many others. But the Comet I was doomed. Its greatly changed successor, the Comet IV, did not fly until 1958, when it still added lustre to the Comet name by inaugurating the first transatlantic jet passenger service.

Jet lift, long dreamed of even by Victorian scientists, was finally harnessed and collared in the Rolls-Royce Vertical Lift Test Rig of 1954. The culmination of this memorable 'bedstead' was the development of the Hawker-Siddeley Harrier.

The Rolls-Royce 'Flying Bedstead' of 1954 was the test rig that led to the development of Vertical Take-off and Land with the astonishing Harrier, now in service in many NATO air forces.

23 LINERS AND WHITE ELEPHANTS

The earliest capacious aeroplane designed for passengers, breathtakingly conceived only two years after the first Russian had flown, was Igor Sikorsky's Bolshoi ('Great'), a biplane with 92ft wing-span powered by four 100hp Argus engines, which accommodated eight people—the pilot and co-pilot in an enclosed cockpit, and the others in armchairs and sofa sitting round a table in a 'greenhouse' cabin glazed with unbreakable glass. This made its first incredible flight in 1913, with high success. Sikorsky developed the Bolshoi into the Ilya Mourometz series of 1914—cabined machines holding 16 people. Seventy-three machines of this type were manufactured. After the outbreak of war some half of the fleet were used as bombers, and only one was shot down.

By 1919 the reverse operation was in progress, with heavy bombers being converted to passenger aircraft. Size was to be a dominant feature in commercial flying, but it was not always the case that 'Big is Beautiful', or even 'Practical'. The Italian Caproni Ca 60 flying-boat, powered by eight 400hp Liberty engines, an enormous triple triplane with room for 100 passengers, flew only twice in two years and had to be abandoned. The great Dornier Do X flying-boat of 1929 had a wing-span half as wide again at 157ft, when it took off on a proving trial from Lake Constance, powered by 12 550hp Siemens (Bristol) Jupiter radial engines in six nacelles, with one pulling and one pushing. It carried 169 people: 10 crew, 150 passengers and

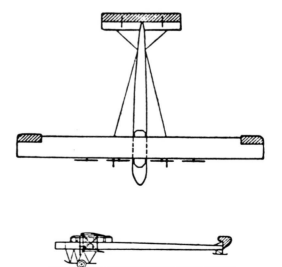

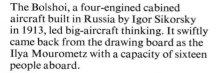

The Bolshoi, a four-engined cabined aircraft built in Russia by Igor Sikorsky in 1913, led big-aircraft thinking. It swiftly came back from the drawing board as the Ilya Mourometz with a capacity of sixteen people aboard.

nine stowaways! But its normal complement was 40 first-class passengers only, for the thirties was the decade of space and comfort, as is indicated by the Pullman ambience of the Handley Page four-engined HP42, the old-style biplane that was the backbone of Imperial Airways at that time.

The first true air 'liner' of modern configuration was the Boeing 247, which even in 1933 was derived from a bomber, the Boeing B-9, and carried only 10 passengers. It was the first transport to have

Nine wings of 100ft span were designed for the Caproni Ca 60, intended as a passenger aircraft taking 100 people. But the drag exercised by the wings and struts of the triple triplane was too much even for eight engines to master, and the 2-year life of the machine, from 1919 to 1921, was graced only by two flights.

The Dornier Do X flying-boat was the largest aeroplane in existence when it took off from Lake Constance in 1929, with nine stowaways adding weight to its 160 crew and passengers. Only three machines of this type were built.

Before aircraft vied with sardine tins, this was the roomy accommodation in the HP42, the famous Imperial Airways luxury work-horse before World War II.

The new look came into commercial airline flying along with new specifications of reliability in the clean monoplane Boeing 247 of 1933.

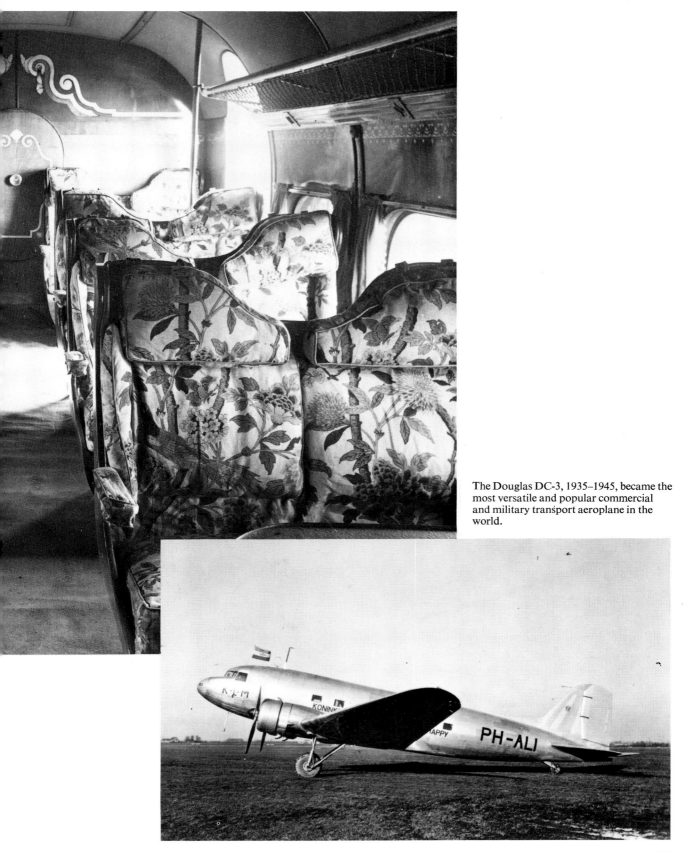

The Douglas DC-3, 1935–1945, became the most versatile and popular commercial and military transport aeroplane in the world.

Possessing something of the massive pretentiousness of the Moscow Metro, Tupolev's ANT-20 *Maxim Gorky* (1934) is seen flying over the Kremlin with escorts that were later to dash it to the ground. It had six 900hp M-34FRN twelve-cylinder engines mounted in the wings, and two more mounted in tandem on top of the fuselage. The aircraft had a life of 365 days.

It flew just once—for 1,000yd. The largest aircraft ever to be airborne is (for it still exists), the Hughes Hercules of 1946, designed and eventually piloted by the late Howard Hughes, and specified as having accommodation for 700 passengers, but with no windows in the cabin.

The 130-ton Bristol Brabazon, 1949, with
a wing-span of 230ft and a height of 50ft
to the top of the fin, never went into
service, being overtaken by postwar
airline requirements, although it had a
potential range of 5,500 miles. Coming in to
land at Farnborough, it shares the air with
the hulk of the tree to which S. F. Cody
used to tether his aircraft, 40 years
previously, while he tested their engines.

157

rubber de-icing equipment on the wings and tail unit. It was rivalled, and eventually matched, by the Douglas DC-1 and its derivative Douglas DC-3, carrying 21 passengers up to some 500 miles in a stage. The DC-3, produced from 1935 to 1945 (and also known militarily as the C-47 and, by the Royal Air Force, as the Dakota), was so overpoweringly successful a machine that 13,000 had been built by the time it went out of production.

Meanwhile in Russia Andrei N. Tupolev produced the gigantic ANT-20, *Maxim Gorky*, a 41-ton monoplane powered by eight engines, which required a crew of 23 to minister to its 40 passengers. The *Maxim Gorky* had a life of just 365 days. It first flew on 19 May 1934, and it crashed on 18 May 1935 when it came into collision with an escorting aircraft.

Designed and built between 1942 and 1946, the largest aircraft ever flown—and the biggest white elephant ever conceived—was the Hughes Hercules, sponsored by the eccentric billionaire Howard Hughes. He spent $25 million to develop one master copy of this wooden-hulled monster, with a length of 219ft and a wing-span of 320ft—twice the span of the modern DC-10. The 200-ton aircraft had accommodation for 700 passengers, but flew only at 200mph

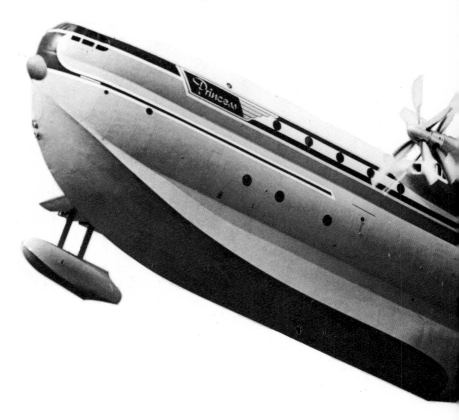

As with the Brabazon, only one Saunders-Roe Princess, 1952, was ever flown, although two others were built. This majestic aircraft was intended for the Southampton–New York service, but it was decreed that the age of flying-boats was past.

from the drive of eight 28-cylinder 3,000hp radial engines. Hughes, however, thought there was more money to be made by confining the services of the Hercules to freight carriage, so he deliberately built no cabin windows in his prototype. The billionaire personally flew this aircraft once, for 1,000yd over the harbour at Los Angeles, and the Hercules has been preserved in mothballs ever since.

There is more than faulty design among the factors that can declare a flying machine unsuitable. Two beautiful aircraft, the Brabazon of 1949 and the Princess of 1952, fell victims to the competitive march of science and to Great Britain's financial debility after World War II, as well as to design problems that could eventually have been mastered. The Brabazon, built by the Bristol Aircraft Company, was an enormous machine only 40ft short of the length of the Hughes Hercules and 20ft higher, and roads and houses at Filton had to be destroyed to extend the runway to get it into the air. Eight Centaurus radial piston engines were coupled to drive four pairs of contra-rotating propellers. A contra-rotating arrangement was also adopted for eight of the ten propellers of the Princess, made by Saunders-Roe, the engines here being Bristol Proteus Series 600 turboprops. Undoubtedly this pairing feature threw up difficulties in both aircraft that it would have been expensive to surmount. The Princess was intended to extend Great Britain's old supremacy in flying-boat design and passenger operation, but the world aircraft business was turning away from flying-boat operation and, further to clinch the rejection of the Brabazon, away from piston-engine drive. The solitary Brabazon flew for only 400 hours in four years. The graceful Princess saluted the Farnborough Air Show like a swan—and the project died in the song of her engines.

24 PILOTED ROCKETS: A MATTER OF LIFE AND DEATH

Rocket propulsion had been used, for a model aircraft, as early as 1420, when the Italian engineer Fontana constructed a bird-shaped rocket head. Modern rocketry, theoretically outlined by the American Dr R. H. Goddard in 1926, was given practical form in 1928 when Fritz von Opel, among others, financed an aeroplane that flew for a mile, and in 1929 a glider that reached 100mph. In 1944 the Messerschmitt Me 163 Komet rocket-propelled fighter was used in action over Germany, and the Japanese rocket-propelled winged bomb navigated (suicidally) by a pilot was used in the *Kamikaze* attacks on the United States fleets in the Pacific. But the most amazing development of rocket propulsion in piloted aircraft was the German Ba 349 Natter, designed by Erich Bachem and operated towards the end of World War II. This was to be rocket-launched vertically from a tower and radio-controlled to a position about a mile away from a bomber fleet. At this point the pilot was to take over and fire 24 rockets at the enemy. This done, he was to release a mechanism that broke up the machine in flight and ejected him by parachute, with the less-expendable rear part of the fuselage containing the rocket engine descending on a parallel parachute. On the first occasion the Natter was used the pilot was killed through a mechanical fault, but a small number of interceptions of this nature were in fact carried out.

Flight research into aircraft travelling at extreme speeds (4,500mph) and rising to great altitudes (250,000ft) culminated in the construction of the North American X-15, a rocket-powered piloted aircraft launched in mid-air from a modified Boeing B-52 and propelled by liquid oxygen and anhydrous ammonia. By 1963 this machine had exceeded the required altitude by reaching 314,750ft, and in October 1967 it exceeded the required speed, making 4,534mph or Mach 6·72.

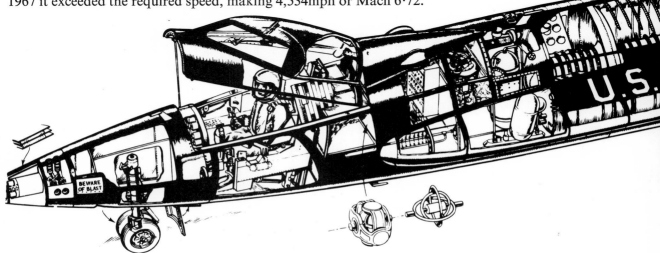

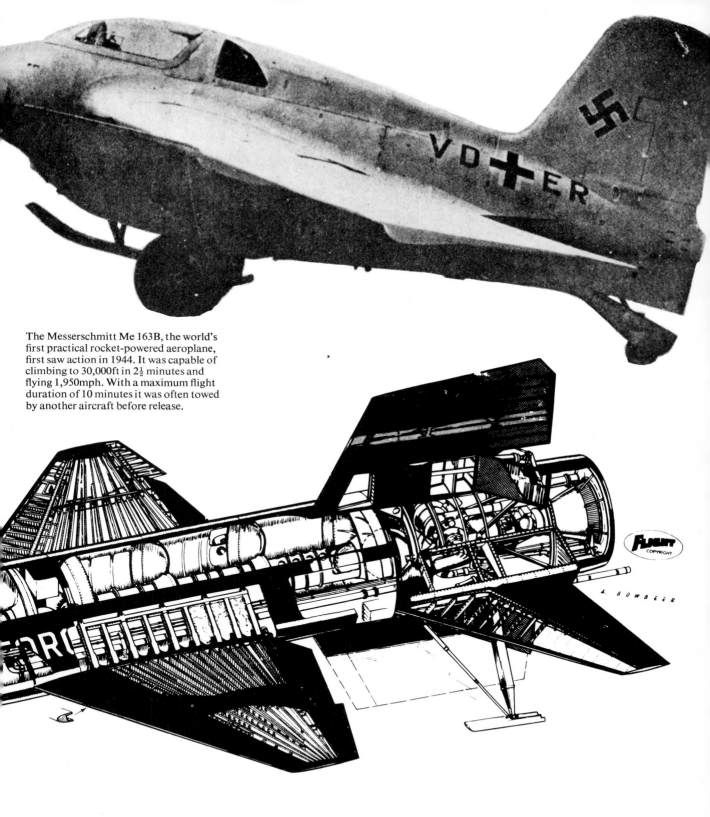

The Messerschmitt Me 163B, the world's first practical rocket-powered aeroplane, first saw action in 1944. It was capable of climbing to 30,000ft in 2½ minutes and flying 1,950mph. With a maximum flight duration of 10 minutes it was often towed by another aircraft before release.

This piloted rocket-propelled North American X-15 has reached a speed of 4,534mph.

25 TWO QUESTION MARKS OF 1977

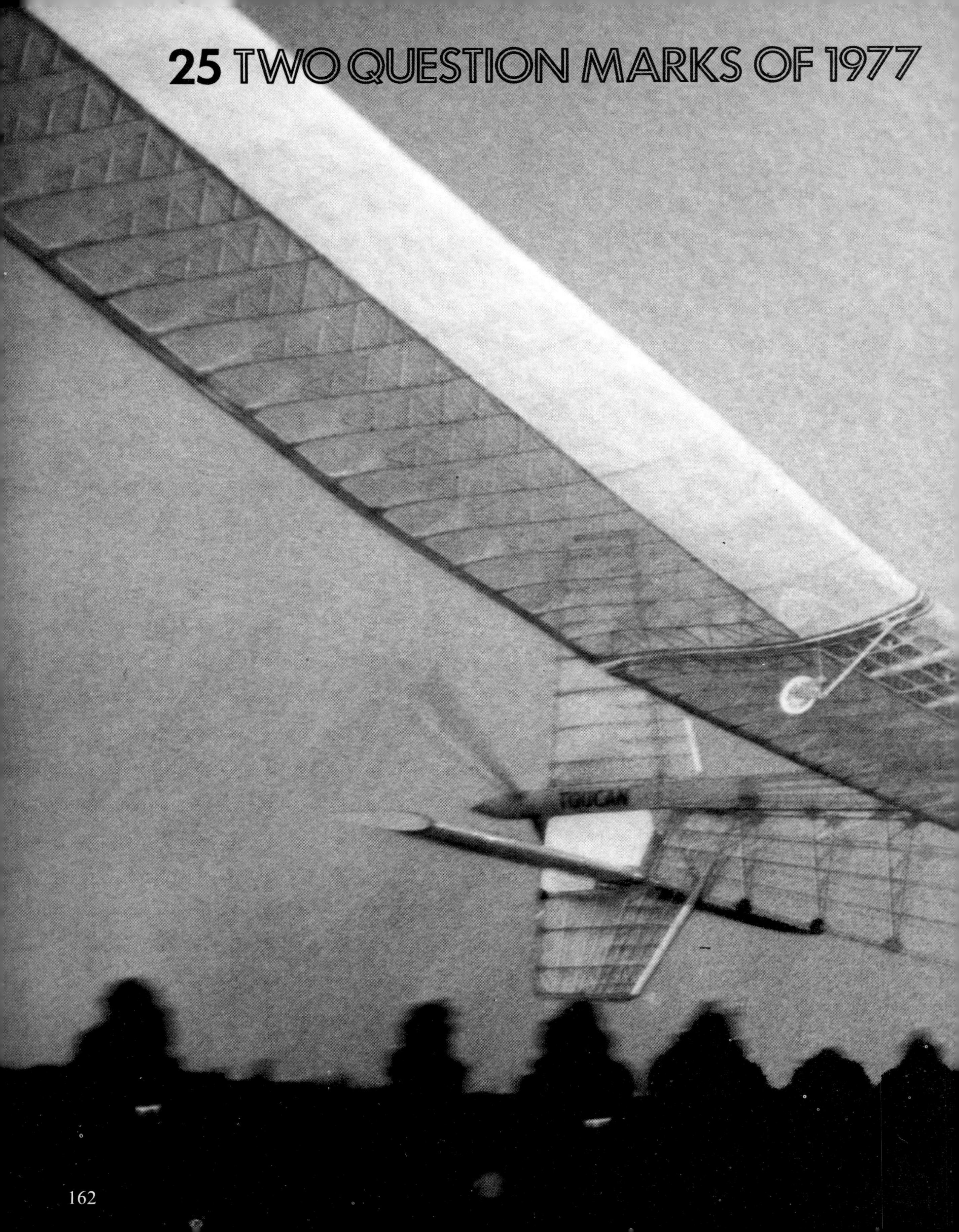

Here is the Toucan, manned by a crew of two from the Hertfordshire Pedal Aeronauts—a team who are not so nutty as their Sherlock Holmes style title suggests, and are mainly composed of professional aircraft engineers and pilots. The latest 'development' of flying is not far from where man once started this once-impossible dream. In the beginning he built wings and tried to learn to flap them like a bird. Now he has learned that birds fly by screwing their muscles into the changing air, and relishing the delights of soaring between intervals of damned hard work. He has learned, too, from a deeper study of anatomy and ergonomics, that power for man's flight must, by the laws of energy and the puny state of the human pectoral muscle, come from nothing less direct than a propeller or a jet. The Hertfordshire Pedal Aeronauts, while no doubt pondering with many other enthusiasts the possibility of creating such a reaction jet in the human gut that the perpetrator becomes instantly airborne, have for the moment concentrated on the propeller, and have favoured human thighs rather than biceps for activating it. The pedal-propelled Toucan seen here making a flight of 700yd in 1973 crashed disastrously on landing. But 66 years previously—less than one man's lifetime—Santos-Dumont and Blériot were crashing just as desperately after flying much shorter distances. Yet two years later the flight records stood at 47.85mph speed, (Blériot); 145.59 miles distance (Henry Farman); and 1,486ft height (Latham). The Blériot, Farman and Antoinette machines were assiduously redesigned and rebuilt. So was the Toucan. Their successors have soared again, and so has man. In 1977 four national teams were sweating to grab the £50,000 Kremer Prize for a figure-of-eight man-powered flight. Toucan Two was being re-assembled after another crash, but the betting odds were on the solo Japanese pedal-pilot Takashi Kato. While also in 1977 the future of Concorde, the world's first supersonic airliner, hangs in the balance.

ACKNOWLEDGEMENTS

For permission to reproduce photographs we wish to thank the following: Air Portraits, pp 118–19, 132–3; British Aircraft Corporation, pp 156–7; The British Museum, London, pp 13, 23; Don L Brown, pp 142–3; Flight International, pp 74 (above and below), 77 (left), 104–5, 110–11, 123, 124–5, 134, 141, 144–5, 146–7, 148–9, 149 (above left), 152–3 (above), 158–9, 160–1; Keystone Press Agency, pp 19, 155; The Mansell Collection, pp 11, 12, 14, 15 (left and right), 89 (below); The National Motor Museum Beaulieu, pp 58, 59, 63; Ron Moulton, pp 162–3; Qantas Airways Ltd, pp 51, 52; Radio Times Hulton Picture Library, pp 27, 29, 33, 44 (above, centre and below), 48 (above), 91 (above), 108, 114–15, 128–9; Rolls-Royce, p 149 (above right); The Royal Aeronautical Society, pp 57 (below), 67 (above and below), 69, 71, 75, 80 (below), 81, 90, 91 (below), 97, 99, 101 (above), 105 (below), 106, 107, 114 (above), 122, 127, 130, 132 (above), 135, 137, 138, 138–9, 142 (above), 151 (above and below), 152 (below left), 153 (below right); Science Museum, London, pp 8, 17, 21, 25, 31, 32, 36, 38, 39, 41, 47, 48 (below), 49 55, 56, 62, 68, 72, 76, 84–5, 88, 89 (above), 92–3, 94, 95, 96, 104 (below), 121; Tass Press Agency, p 154; Torbay Aircraft Museum/Hawker Siddeley Aviation Ltd., pp 116, 117; Torbay Aircraft Museum/British Aircraft Corporation, pp 164–5; Reproduced by courtesy of Charles H. Gibbs-Smith, pp 40, 50, 53, 57 (above), 66, 77 (right), 80 (above), 101 (below), 102 (below), 103, 112, 113, 131, 140, 150, 161 (above).

INDEX